50 Quick-Play Articulation Games™

Barb Truman

Lauri Whiskeyman

Skill Area:	Articulation
Age Level:	5 thru 10
Grades:	K thru 5

LinguiSystems

LinguiSystems, Inc.
3100 4th Avenue
East Moline, IL 61244

Web: linguisystems.com
FAX: 800-577-4555
email: service@linguisystems.com

800-776-4332

ISBN 10: 0-7606-0478-9
ISBN 13: 978-0-7606-0478-6

About the Authors

Barb Truman, M.A., CCC-SLP and **Lauri Whiskeyman**, M.A., Ed.S, CCC-SLP are speech-language pathologists who worked with children in preschool through high school before joining the LinguiSystems family. At LinguiSystems, they help develop products, field questions from customers, and staff booths at conventions. Barb and Lauri are also co-authors of *Scissors, Glue, and Vocabulary, Too!* and *No-Glamour Articulation*. Barb is also the author of *Barnaby's Burrow* and co-author of *The Auditory Processing Game* and Lauri is the author of *LanguageBurst*.

Dedication

To all the children we've known over the years: you have helped us see new ways to have fun and learn at the same time.

Cover Design by Chris Claus
Page Layout by Jamie Hope
Illustrations by Viki Woodworth and Margaret Warner

Table of Contents

50 Quick-Play Articulation Games

Introduction

50 Quick-Play Articulation Games is just that—50 quick, easy-to-play articulation games for children in kindergarten through 5th grade. The game paths cover the following 21 phonemes:

p, b, m	sh, ch, j
k, g	l, l-blends
t, d	r, r-blends
f, v	s/z
voiceless and voiced th	s-blends

We wanted to give you many games to play with your students, so along with the 50 game paths, we have included directions for 15 card games as well as directions for 11 non-competitive games. As with the game paths, the card games and non-competitive games can be played with one student or several students.

You'll find "cards" for the card games on pages 80 – 173. They include cards for the initial, medial, and final positions of all sounds listed above in both single and multisyllable words. In compiling the card decks, we concentrated on curricular resources and words from everyday life. Using the words your students need to know will better equip you in helping your students meet their curricular goals. You can also use the card grids as is for drill, or copy them and send them home for practice.

To create a 52-card deck, you'll need to copy one grid four times, or copy four different grids, depending on your students' needs. Each card has a small circle in the corner. Color-code your cards by coloring the circles different colors. For example, color all of the circles on one grid red, the next grid blue, etc. Then cut apart the cards.

In addition, we have included a generic game path for you to create your own game (page 178), and a page with stars to use as a motivational, fun sheet for students to color as they practice their articulation (page 179).

Your students will have fun, and you'll enjoy the variety in *50 Quick-Play Articulation Games*.

Barb and Lauri

50 Quick-Play Articulation Games

Instructions for Game Paths

You can use one die, a spinner, or one coin with the game paths. You will also need a game marker (token) for each player.

The game paths have a word and a picture on each game space. Your students can practice the words alone or use the words in sentences. Here are some suggestions on how to play the games on the game paths:

1. Roll a die. Have the student practice the word (sentence) on each space as he moves his token the number of spaces shown on the die.

2. Roll a die. Have the student say one word (sentence) correctly and then move the number of spaces shown on the die.

3. Roll a die. Have the student choose one of the words (sentences) from the game board to practice as he moves his token the number of spaces shown on the die. He should then say the word the number of times shown on the die.

4. Roll a die. Have the student move ahead for even numbers and back for odd numbers. The student should practice each word (sentence) he passes while moving forward or backward.

5. Have each student begin by saying the first word on the game path. Then have him flip a coin. He moves one space for heads and two spaces for tails. (This is especially good for shorter paths/longer games/more practice!)

If a student misarticulates a word (sentence), you can have the student:

- Say the word (sentence) again. If correct, he moves the same as he would have on the first attempt.

- Roll the die again and say the misarticulated word(s) the number of times shown on the die.

- Lose his turn.

50 Quick-Play Articulation Games

Parker's Pizzas

Help Parker deliver his pizzas. Remember to say your /p/ sound correctly.

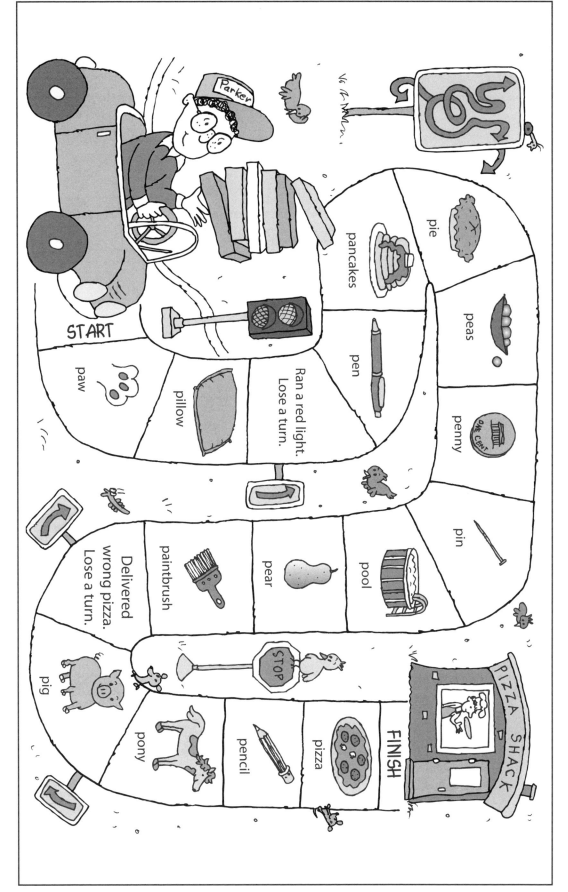

START

paw

pillow

Ran a red light. Lose a turn.

pen

pancakes

pie

peas

penny

pin

pool

pear

paintbrush

Delivered wrong pizza. Lose a turn.

pig

STOP

pony

pencil

pizza

FINISH

PIZZA SHACK

50 Quick-Play Articulation Games

7

Copyright © 2003 LinguiSystems, Inc.

The Lost Cap

Hap lost his baseball cap. Can you help him find it? Remember to say your /p/ sound correctly.

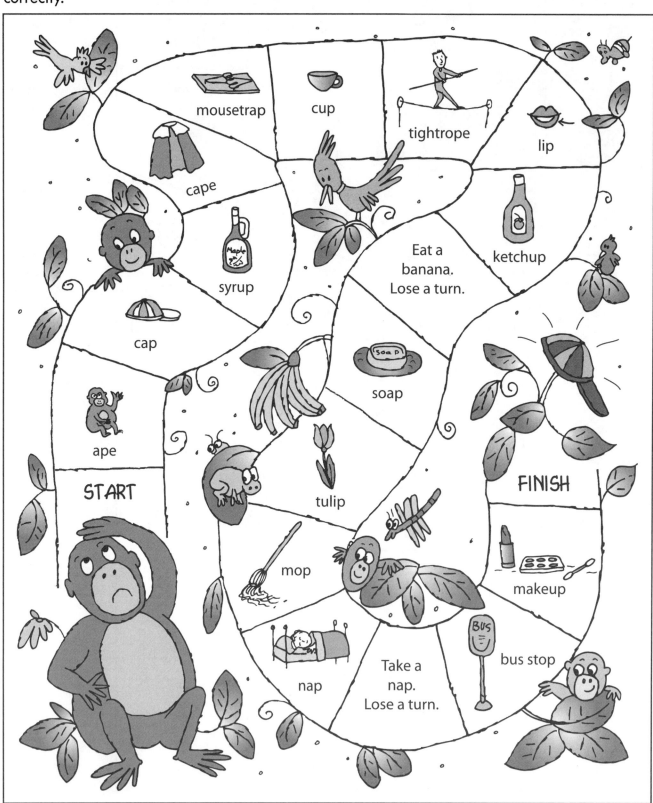

Play Ball!

Help Becca play basketball. Remember to say your /b/ sound correctly.

initial /b/
50 Quick-Play Articulation Games

Find the Globe

Jacob needs a globe for social studies. Do you know where he can find one? Remember to say your /b/ sound correctly.

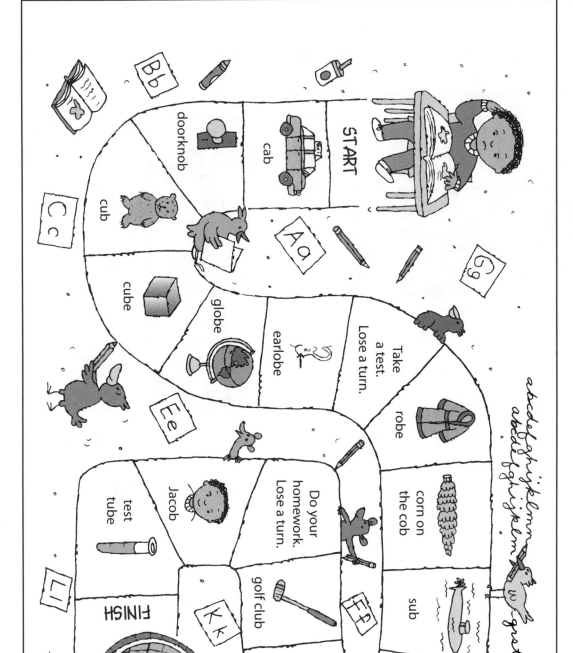

START

cab

doorknob

cub

Cc

cube

Bb

Aa

Gg

globe

earlobe

Take a test. Lose a turn.

robe

corn on the cob

sub

ice cube

Ee

Jacob

test tube

Do your homework. Lose a turn.

golf club

Ff

tub

web

FINISH

Ll

Kk

Jj

Ii

Hh

abcdefghijklmn
abcdefghijklm
nopqrstuvwxyz

final /b/
50 Quick-Play Articulation Games

Eek — A Mouse!

Max is afraid of mice. Help him get home safely. Remember to say your /m/ sound correctly.

initial /m/
50 Quick-Play Articulation Games

Sam's Jam

Sam wants some jam on her toast. Can you help her find some? Remember to say your /m/ sound correctly.

A Hungry Caterpillar

Say each word on the caterpillar using your good /k/ sound.

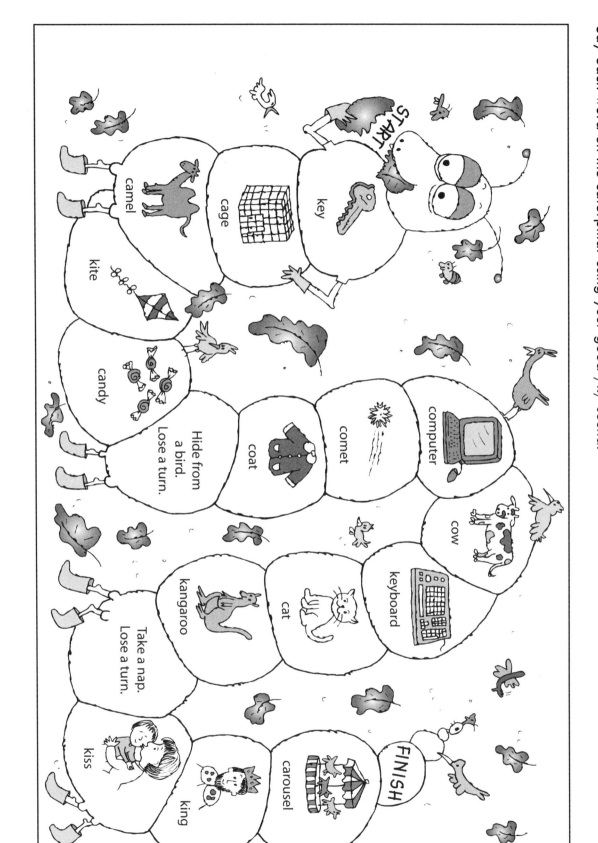

initial /k/
50 Quick-Play Articulation Games

Jake's Homework

Oh no! Jake's homework is blowing away! Use a good /k/ sound as you help him find all of the pages.

final /k/
50 Quick-Play Articulation Games

Pumpkin Patch

Use your good /k/ sound as you help Nicholas find a pumpkin.

Go-Carting!

Use your good /g/ sound to get the go-cart around the track.

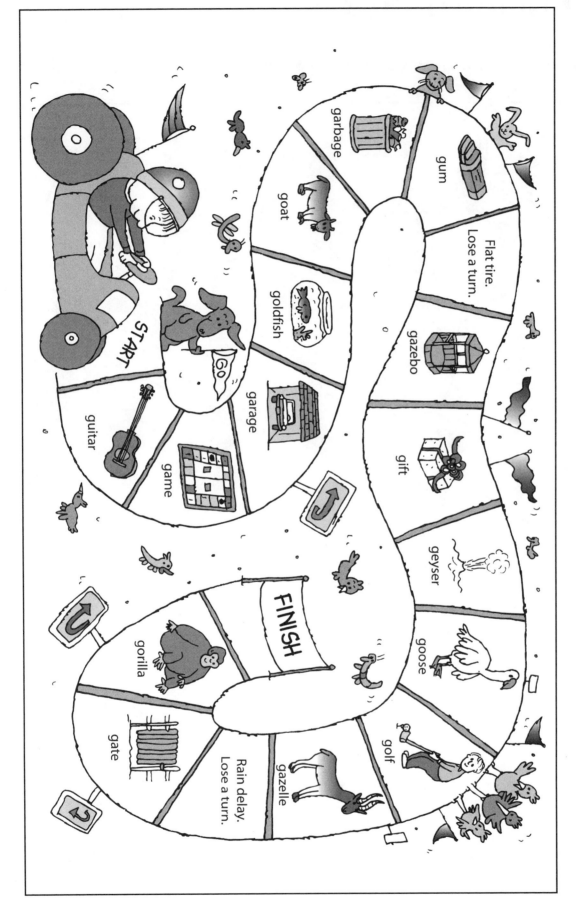

Looking for Bones

Use your good /g/ sound as this dog finds his bones.

START

Chased by a cat. Lose a turn.

polliwog

bug

sleeping bag

pig

peg

ladybug

duffel bag

FINISH

twig

rug

egg

hug

catalog

paper bag

hot dog

flag

Time for a walk. Lose a turn.

final /g/
50 Quick-Play Articulation Games

17

Copyright © 2003 LinguiSystems, Inc.

The Dragon's Cave

Use your good /g/ sound to help the dragon get to his cave.

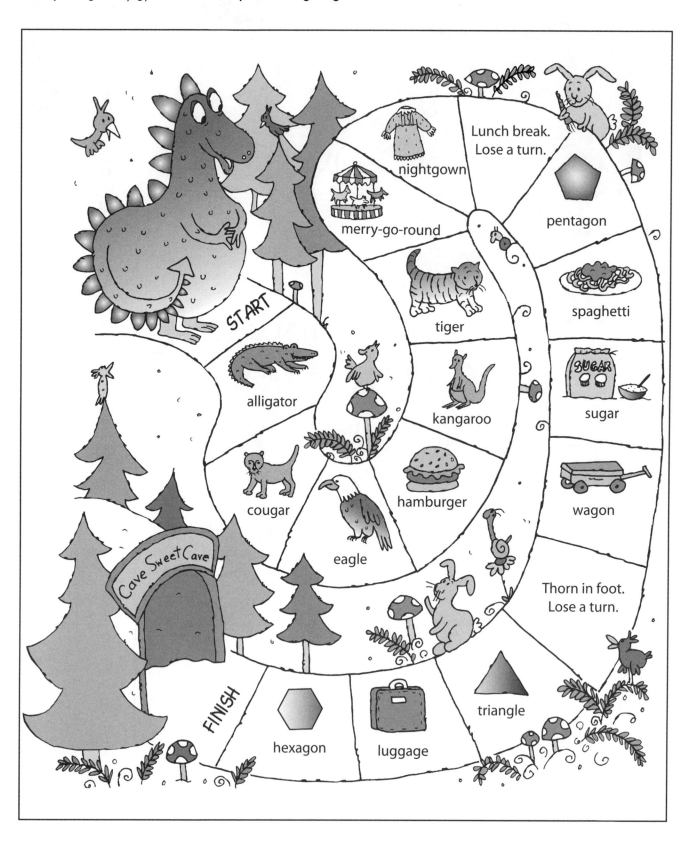

Terrell's Tree House

Terrell built a tree house. Help him climb to the top. Remember to say your /t/ sound correctly.

initial /t/
50 Quick-Play Articulation Games

Kate's Cat

Kate is looking for her cat. Will you help her? Remember to say your /t/ sound correctly.

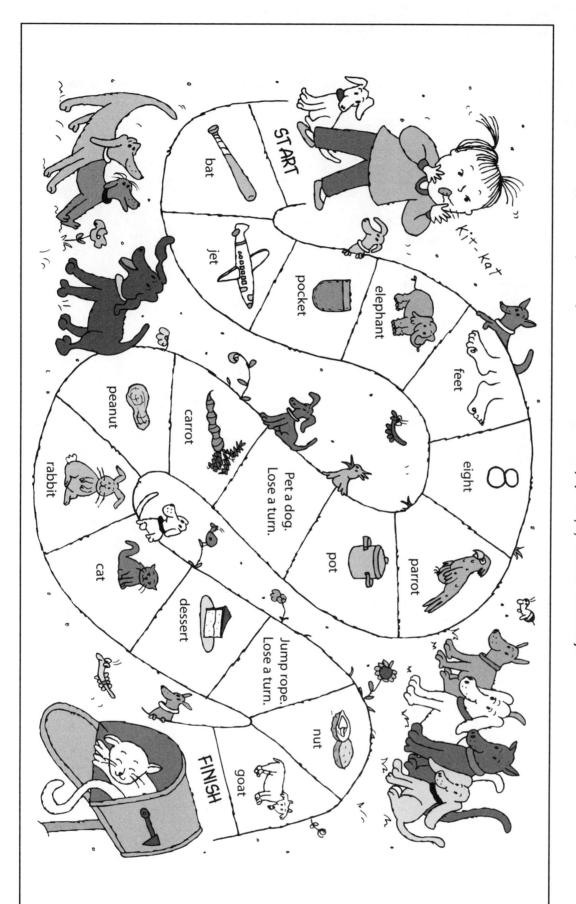

START
bat
jet
pocket
elephant
feet
eight
parrot
pot
Pet a dog. Lose a turn.
peanut
carrot
rabbit
cat
dessert
Jump rope. Lose a turn.
nut
goat
FINISH

Kit-Kat

Hunter's Turtle

Hunter lost his pet turtle. Help him look for it. Remember to say your /t/ sound correctly.

guitar

alligator

mountains

FINISH

valentine

petal

caterpillar

Stop to watch T.V. Lose a turn.

Jupiter

reptile

50 fifty

October

letters

Answer the phone. Lose a turn.

doctor

equator

55 fifty-five

painter

START

Danny's Dirty Dog

doctor

doughnut

Forgot a towel. Lose a turn.

daisy

dog

dime

doe

dollar

START

dish

dinosaur

Dog chases a cat. Lose a turn.

door

FINISH

donkey

dance

dolphin

duck

dove

The boys are playing hide and seek. Help Ted find Jared. Remember to say your /d/ sound correctly.

START

head

centipede

road

chalkboard

sad

bead

postcard

No one under the desk. Lose a turn.

hand

hide

island

Tripped on a chair. Lose a turn.

salad

lemonade

board

toad

1000 thousand

FINISH

Ladybug Hunt

Help Sydney catch ladybugs. Remember to say your /d/ sound correctly.

medial /d/
50 Quick-Play Articulation Games

Find the Farm

It's time for Philip to go home. Help him find his farmhouse. Remember to say your /f/ sound correctly.

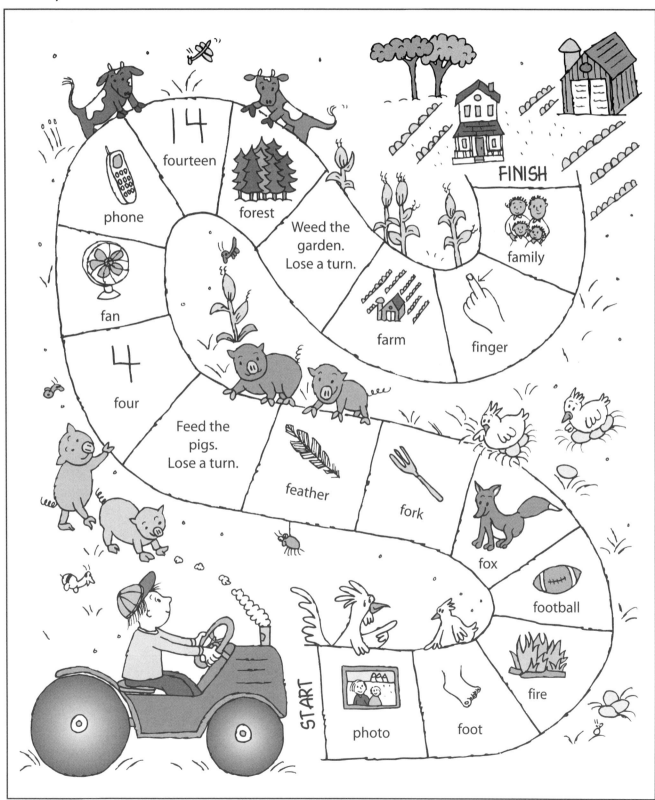

The Lost Elf

This elf has lost his way. Will you help him back to his storybook? Remember to say your /f/ sound correctly.

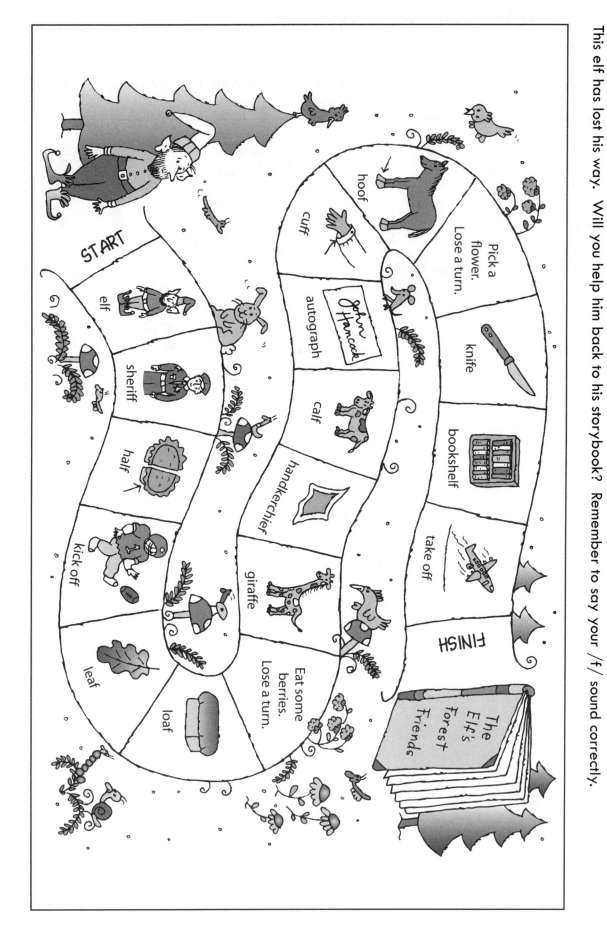

START

elf

sheriff

half

kick off

leaf

loaf

Eat some berries. Lose a turn.

giraffe

handkerchief

calf

autograph

John Hancock

cuff

hoof

Pick a flower. Lose a turn.

knife

bookshelf

take off

FINISH

The Elf's Forest Friends

Sophia Learns the Alphabet

Sophia is learning to say the alphabet. Help her get all the way to Z. Remember to say your /f/ sound correctly along the way.

medial /f/
50 Quick-Play Articulation Games

Victoria's Van

Victoria's mom is waiting in the van. Help Victoria get there. Remember to say your /v/ sound correctly.

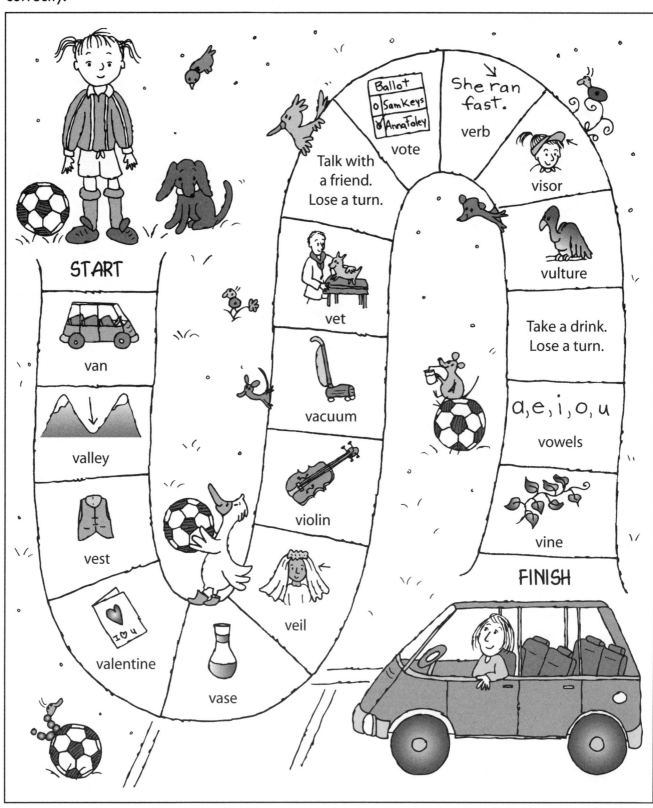

START

van

valley

vest

valentine

vase

veil

violin

vacuum

vet

Talk with a friend. Lose a turn.

vote

Ballot
o SamKeys
✓ AnnaToley

She ran fast.

verb

visor

vulture

Take a drink. Lose a turn.

a, e, i, o, u

vowels

vine

FINISH

initial /v/
50 Quick-Play Articulation Games

Eve and the Beehive

Eve needs your help collecting honey at the beehive. Remember to say your /v/ sound correctly.

Where Is That Elevator?

Steven is looking for the elevator. Help him find it by saying your /v/ sound correctly.

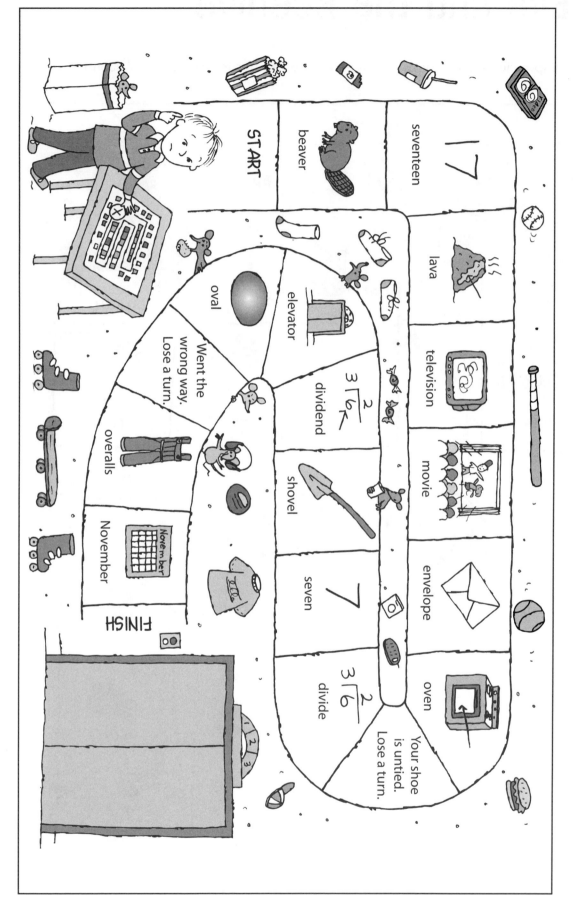

START

beaver

seventeen | 17

lava

television

movie

envelope

oven

Your shoe is untied. Lose a turn.

divide | $3\overline{)6}$ $\frac{2}{}$

seven | 7

shovel

dividend | $3\overline{)6}$ $\frac{2}{}$

elevator

oval

Went the wrong way. Lose a turn.

overalls

November

FINISH

It's a Jungle Out There!

Theo is lost in a number jungle! Use a good /th/ sound as you help him find his way out.

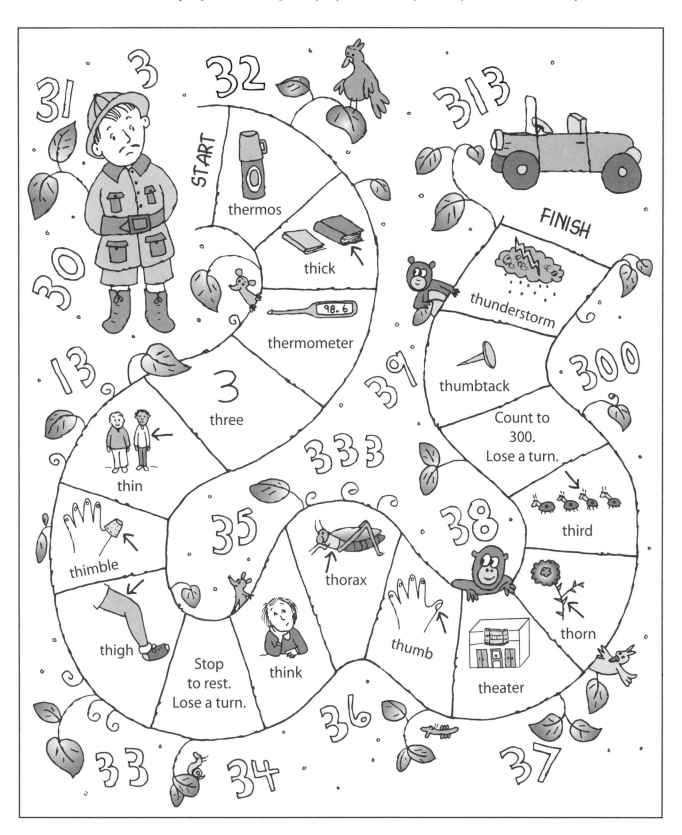

Flying South

Use your good /th/ sound as Beth flies south for the winter.

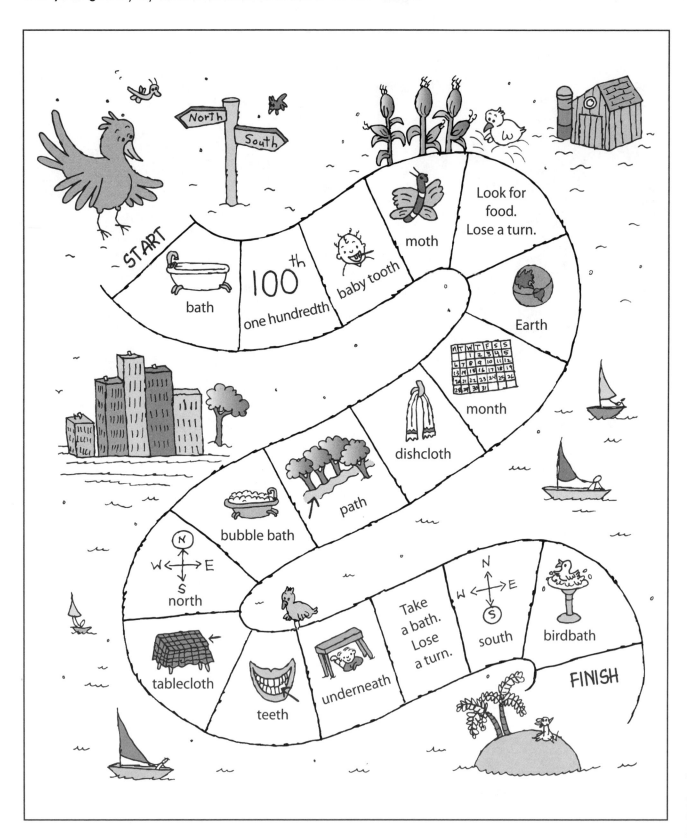

Don't Slip!

Kathy didn't dry off very well after her bath. Use your good /th/ sound as you help wipe up the puddles.

The game board contains the following spaces:

START

- athlete
- southwest
- toothpaste
- author
- panther
- bath towel
- math class
- stethoscope
- Forgot your bathrobe. Lose a turn.
- python
- southeast
- bathtub
- Slipped on the water. Lose a turn.
- birthday
- (and me) parenthesis
- mouthful
- toothbrush

FINISH

Kathy's Room

medial voiceless /th/
50 Quick-Play Articulation Games

Raking Leaves

Help the girl rake leaves. Don't forget to use your good /th/ sound!

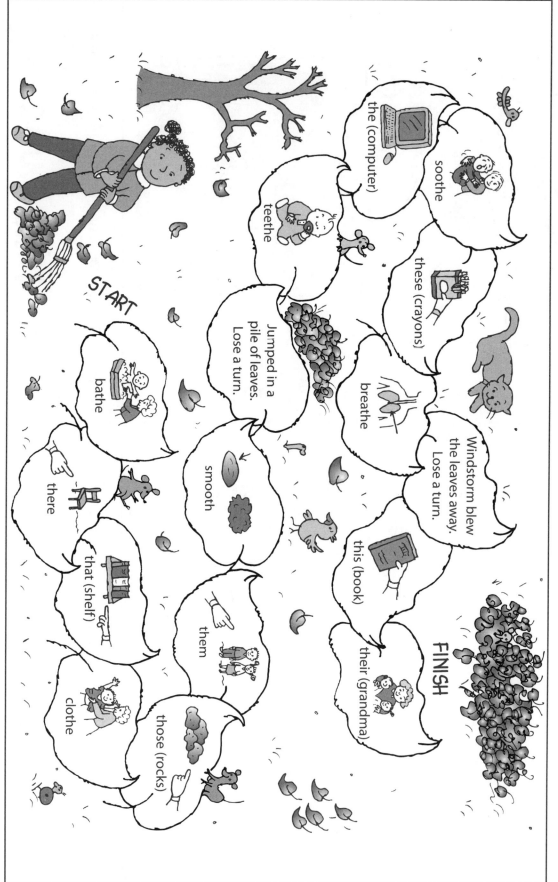

initial/final voiced /th/
50 Quick-Play Articulation Games

Gathering Eggs

This chicken laid too many eggs. Gather them up as you use your good /th/ sound.

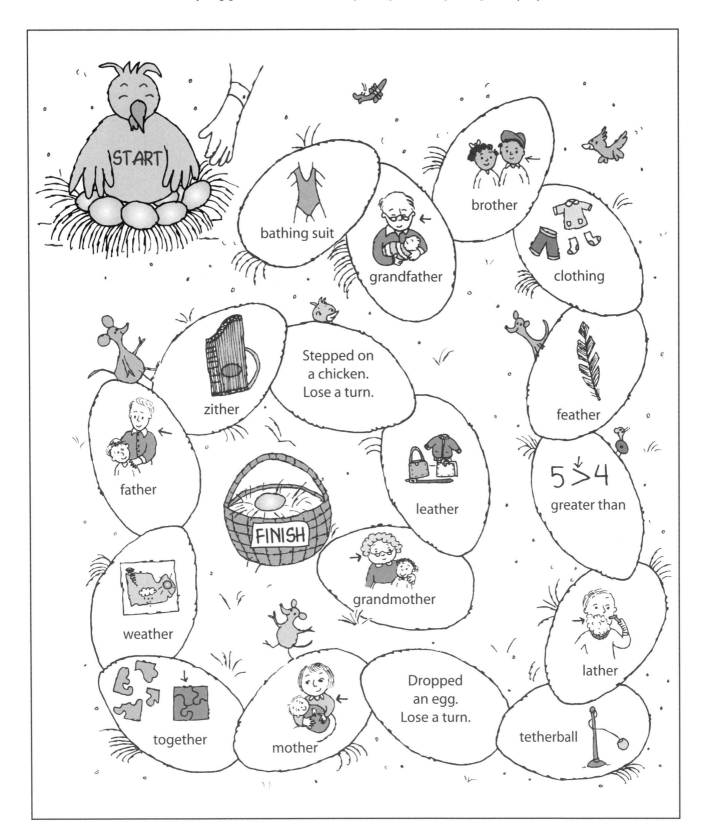

medial voiced /th/
50 Quick-Play Articulation Games

Show Time

Help Shane get to the show. Be sure to use your good /sh/ sound along the way.

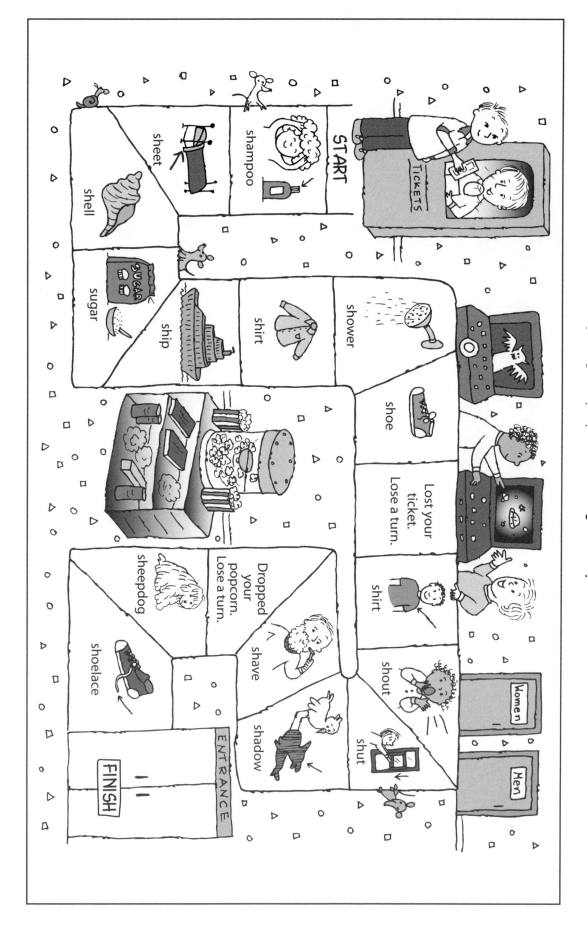

START

TICKETS

sheet
shell
shampoo
sugar
ship
shirt
shower
shoe
Lost your ticket. Lose a turn.
shirt
shout
shut
shadow
shave
Dropped your popcorn. Lose a turn.
sheepdog
shoelace
ENTRANCE
FINISH
Women
Men

initial /sh/
50 Quick-Play Articulation Games

Splish-Splash!

Josh and his family are at Splish-Splash Water Park. Use a good /sh/ sound as Josh goes down the water slide.

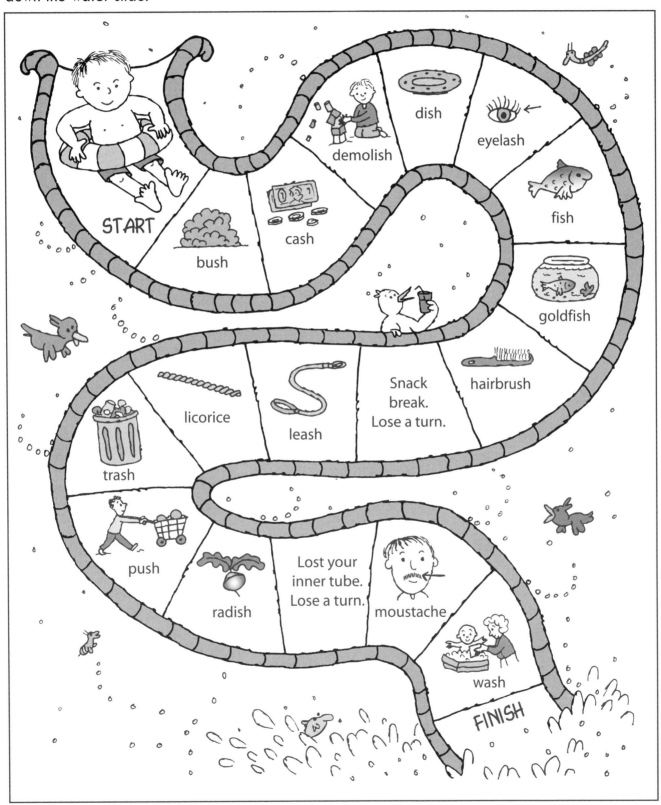

final /sh/
50 Quick-Play Articulation Games

Gone Fishing

Marshall is a fisherman. Use your good /sh/ sound to help him catch some fish.

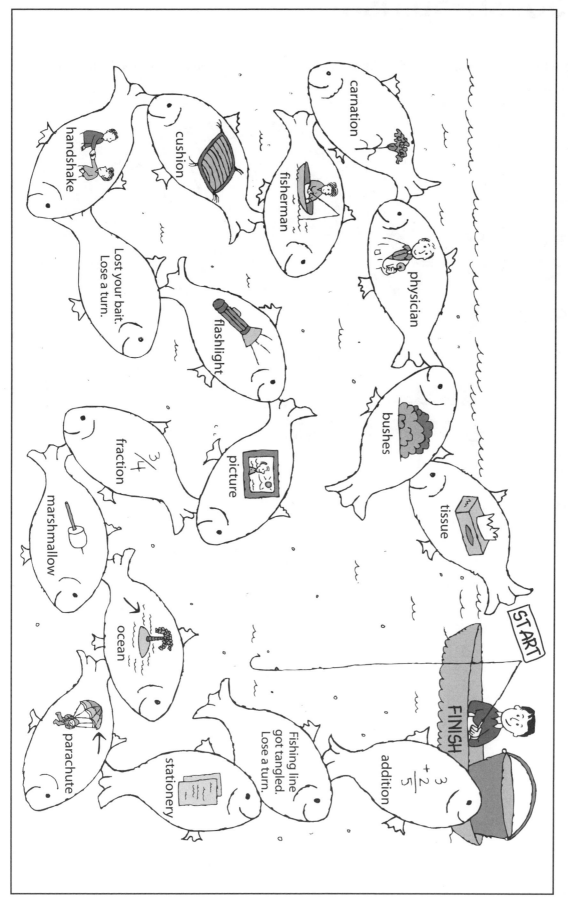

Labels within the game board:

- carnation
- handshake
- cushion
- fisherman
- Lost your bait. Lose a turn.
- flashlight
- physician
- bushes
- picture
- fraction 3/4
- tissue
- marshmallow
- ocean
- parachute
- stationery
- Fishing line got tangled. Lose a turn.
- addition 3 + 2/5
- START
- FINISH

Time for Lunch!

Use your good /ch/ sound as you help Chester get food for lunch. He's really hungry!

initial /ch/
50 Quick-Play Articulation Games

Hopscotch Anyone?

Have fun playing hopscotch with Ollie as you use your good /ch/ sound.

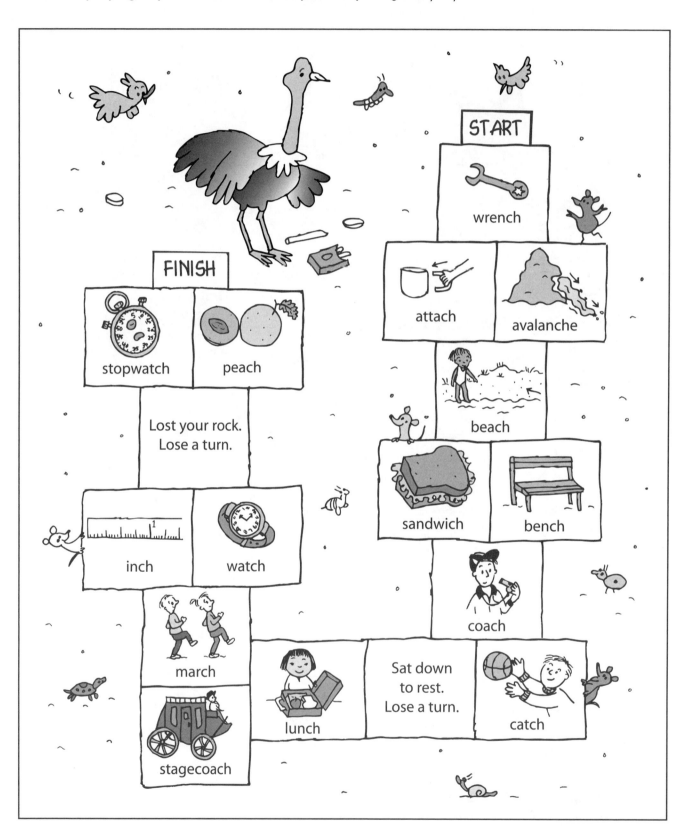

START

wrench

attach

avalanche

beach

sandwich

bench

coach

FINISH

stopwatch

peach

Lost your rock.
Lose a turn.

inch

watch

march

lunch

Sat down
to rest.
Lose a turn.

catch

stagecoach

Creature Feature

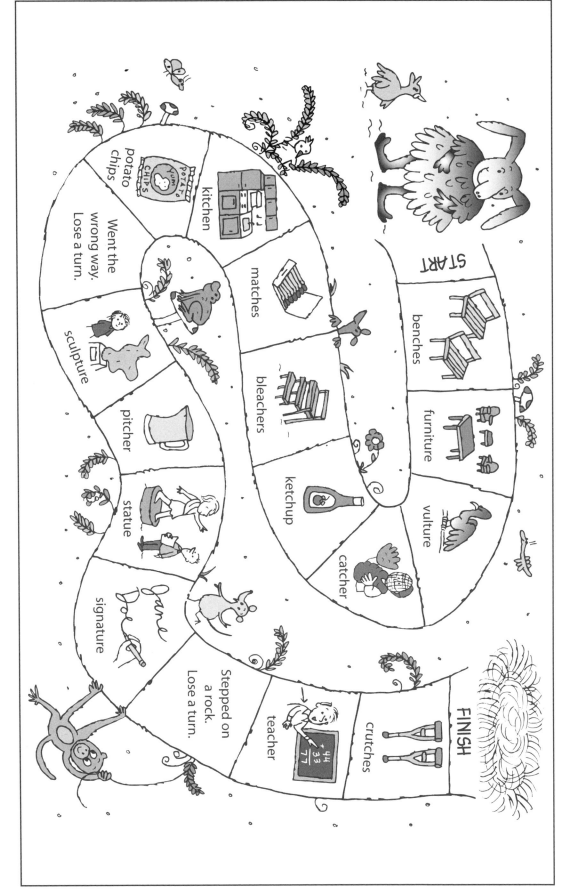

START

benches

furniture

vulture

catcher

ketchup

bleachers

matches

kitchen

potato chips

Went the wrong way. Lose a turn.

sculpture

pitcher

statue

signature

Stepped on a rock. Lose a turn.

teacher

crutches

FINISH

Jump with Jason

Jason is going to jump on his trampoline. Would you like to join him? Remember to say your /j/ sound correctly.

initial /j/
50 Quick-Play Articulation Games

Copyright © 2003 LinguiSystems, Inc.

Yummy Fudge

Help Paige make some fudge. Remember to say your /j/ sound correctly.

START

cage	sausage	hedge
		bridge
		fringe
change	Ran out of sugar. Lose a turn.	bandage	page	orange
carriage				
cottage	badge	Forgot to turn on the stove. Lose a turn.		
package	luggage	fudge		

FINISH

Get Benji Home

Benji is lost. Help him find his way home by remembering to say your /j/ sound correctly.

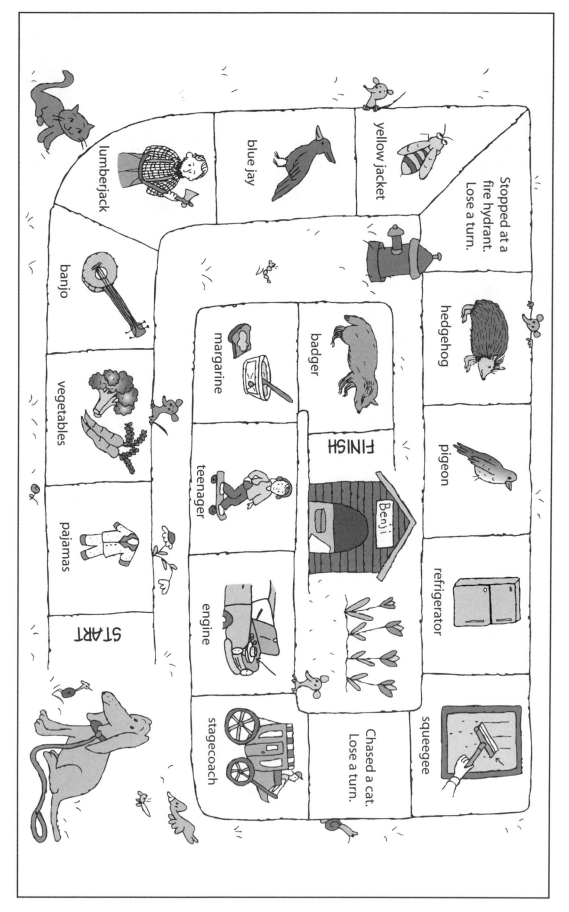

Stopped at a fire hydrant. Lose a turn.

yellow jacket

blue jay

lumberjack

banjo

vegetables

pajamas

START

hedgehog

pigeon

refrigerator

badger

margarine

teenager

engine

FINISH

Benji

squeegee

Chased a cat. Lose a turn.

stagecoach

44

Off to the Library

Use your good /l/ sound as Laura goes to the library.

Ferris Wheel Fun

Use your good /l/ sound as these kids ride on the Ferris wheel.

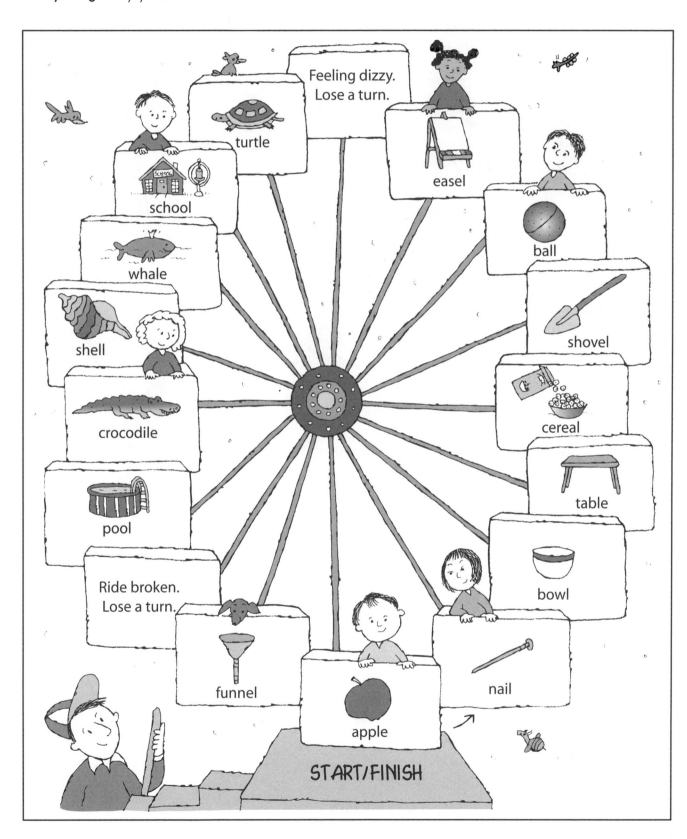

Molly's Balloons

Use your good /l/ sound as you help Molly collect her balloons.

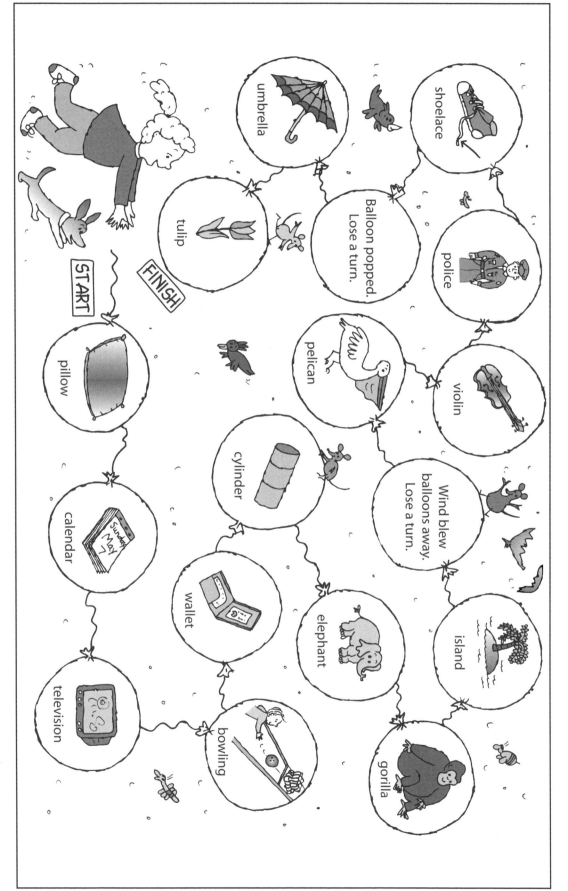

START

FINISH

umbrella

shoelace

tulip

Balloon popped. Lose a turn.

police

pillow

pelican

violin

calendar

cylinder

Wind blew balloons away. Lose a turn.

wallet

elephant

island

television

bowling

gorilla

Playground Fun

Use your good /l/ sound while Blake has fun at the playground.

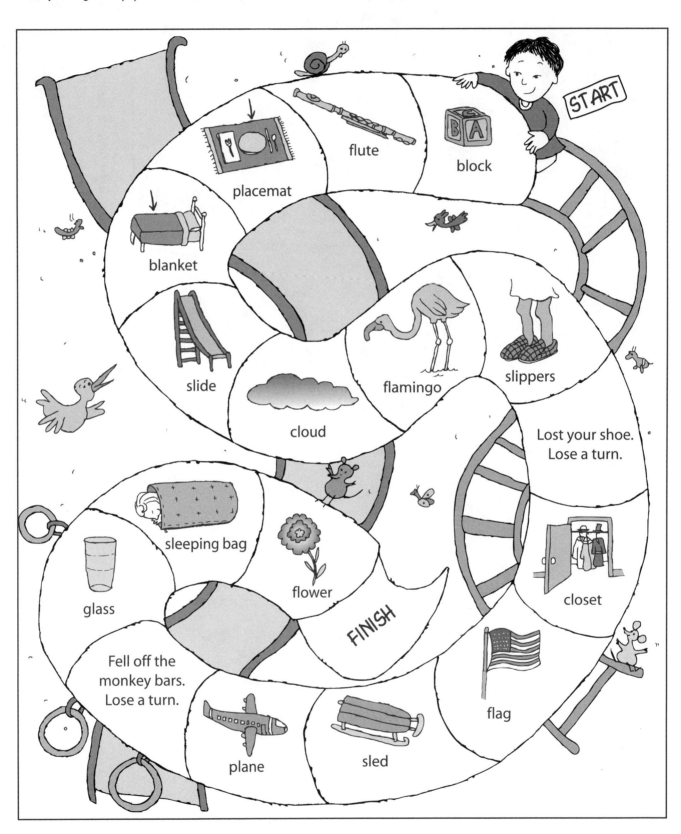

START

flute
block

placemat

blanket

slide

cloud

flamingo

slippers

Lost your shoe.
Lose a turn.

sleeping bag

flower

glass

FINISH

closet

Fell off the
monkey bars.
Lose a turn.

plane

sled

flag

Rachel's Rabbits

Rachel's rabbits have run away. Help her round them up. Remember to say your /r/ sound correctly.

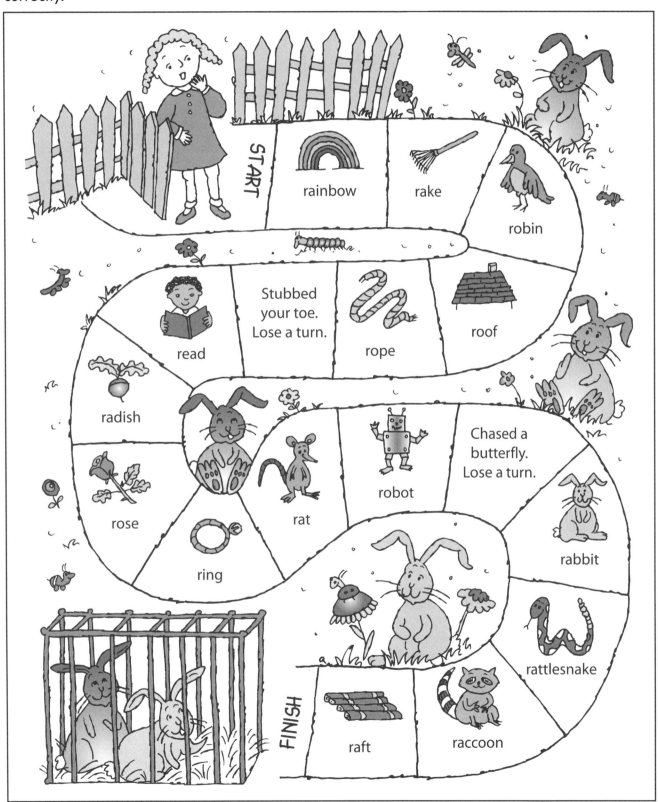

Time for a Haircut

Jennifer is going to get her hair cut. Help her find her way. Remember to say your /r/ sound correctly.

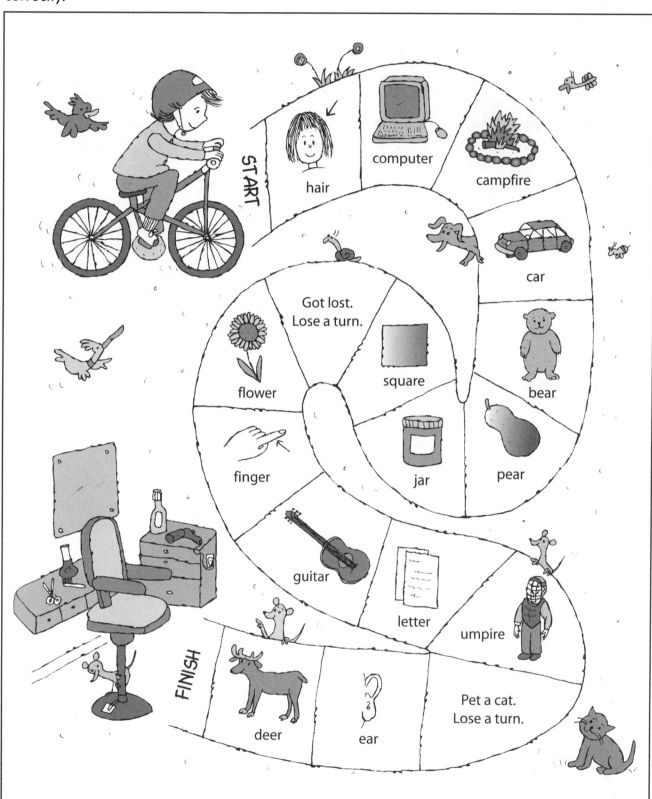

final /r/
50 Quick-Play Articulation Games

Copyright © 2003 LinguiSystems, Inc.

Let's Skydive!

Marissa is learning to skydive. Help her get to the ground safely by remembering to say your /r/ sound correctly.

All About Dragons

Help Christine with her report on dragons. Remember to say your /r/ sound correctly.

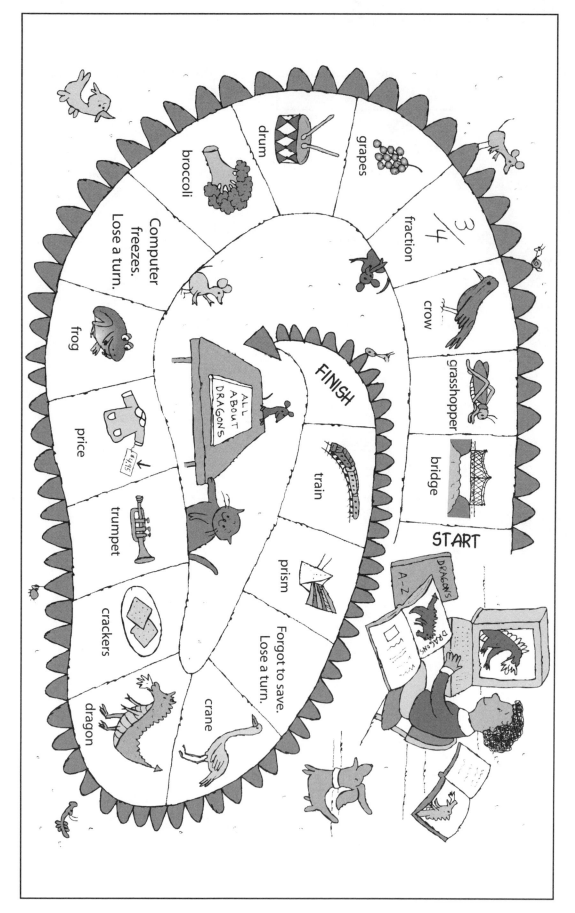

Board game spaces (from START):
- START
- bridge
- grasshopper
- crow
- fraction (3/4)
- grapes
- drum
- broccoli
- Computer freezes. Lose a turn.
- frog
- price
- trumpet
- crackers
- dragon
- crane
- Forgot to save. Lose a turn.
- prism
- train
- FINISH (ALL ABOUT DRAGONS)

initial /r/ blends
50 Quick-Play Articulation Games

Zoe's Trip

Zoe is going to the city. Use your good /s/ and /z/ sounds as she looks at the signs along the way.

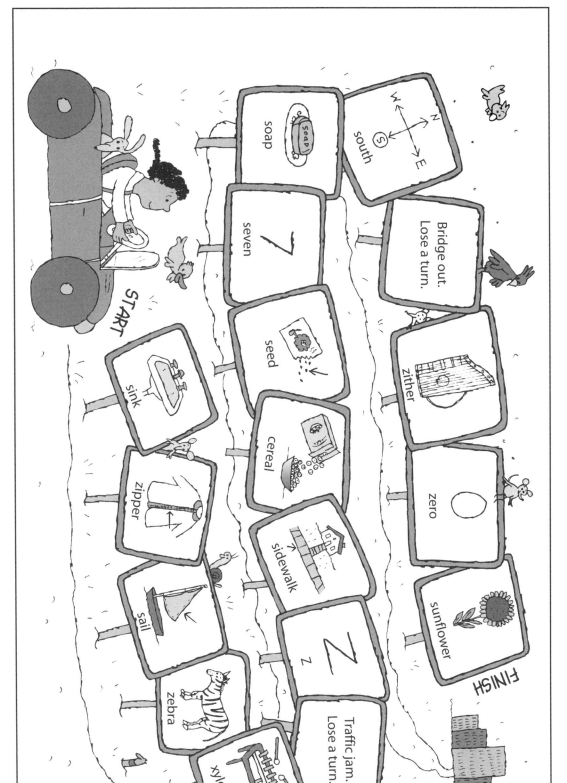

START

soap

south

Bridge out.
Lose a turn.

seven

7

seed

zither

sink

cereal

zero

zipper

sidewalk

sunflower

sail

Z
z

FINISH

zebra

Traffic jam.
Lose a turn.

xylophone

Daisy's Mouse House

Help Daisy find her way to her house. Don't forget to use your good /s/ and /z/ sounds.

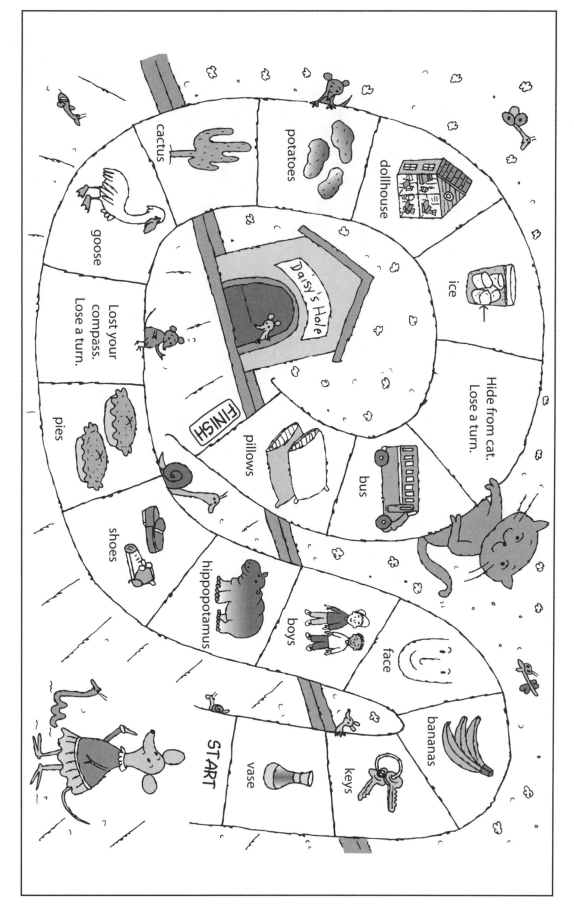

cactus

potatoes

dollhouse

goose

ice

Lost your compass. Lose a turn.

Hide from cat. Lose a turn.

pies

Daisy's Hole

FINISH

pillows

bus

shoes

hippopotamus

boys

face

START

vase

keys

bananas

Puzzle Fun

Use your good /s/ and /z/ sounds as you put the puzzle together.

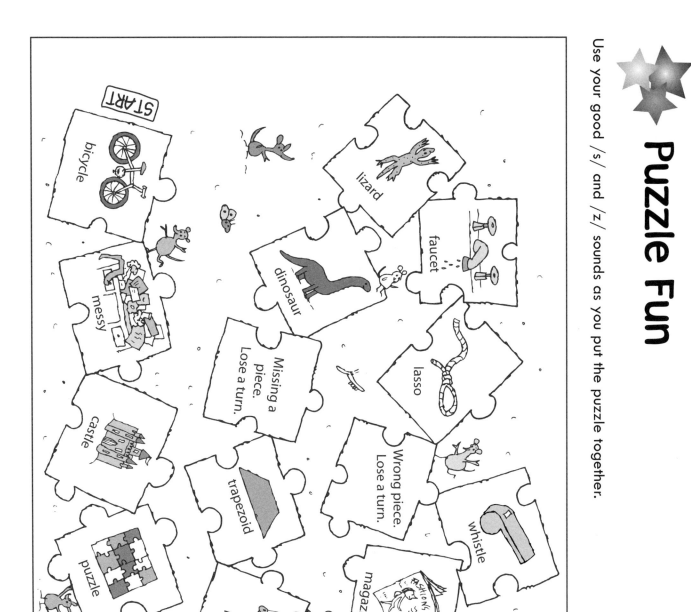

START

bicycle

lizard

faucet

messy

dinosaur

lasso

Missing a piece. Lose a turn.

castle

trapezoid

Wrong piece. Lose a turn.

whistle

puzzle

insect

magazine

daisy

FINISH

present

medicine

Flippin' Pancakes

Help Spencer flip pancakes. Remember to say your /s/ sound correctly.

square

snow

Pancake stuck to the ceiling. Lose a turn.

slippery

starfish

school

swing

scooter

FINISH

Burned the pancakes. Lose a turn.

spatula

snowman

stage

swimming

smile

spoon

slide

stepladder

START

 **1-12-1** (also known as *Ohio*)

Number of Players: two or more

Materials: three dice, a copy of the grid on page 58, a pencil, a different color/type marker for each player, articulation cards

Object of the Game: to be the first to move your marker from the number 1 to 12 and back to number 1

Articulation Practice

- Before the game, have the players say the words on all the cards.

- On each turn, have the player say the word on a card before rolling the dice.

Preparation: Place the stack of articulation cards facedown on the table. Make a copy of the grid on the next page.

To Play: Players roll one die. The player who rolls the highest number goes first. Play proceeds clockwise. The first player turns over the top card, says the word on the card, and rolls all three dice. If one of the dice has a 1 on it, the player moves his marker to the first square. If he doesn't roll a 1, he passes the dice to the next player. Each player must move his marker from square to square in sequence (1, 2, 3, etc.). On each turn, the player tries to throw the number on the next square. The number can be on any one of the dice or reached by adding any or all of the dice together. For example, if a player is on square 3 and he rolls a 1-2-2, he can move to square 4 (2+2). The first player to move from square 1 to square 12 and then back to square 1 is the winner.

Variations: If the player misarticulates the target sound, the next player gets a chance to say it correctly and roll the dice. Play continues clockwise.

For a faster game, allow the players to make several consecutive moves by using all the number options on the dice. (Players must still move from square to square in sequence.) For example, if a player rolls a 1-2-2, he could move to the 1, then the 2, then the 3 (1+2), then the 4 (2+2), and finally the 5 (1+2+2) before play passes to the next player.

1-12-1 Gameboard

1	**7**
2	**8**
3	**9**
4	**10**
5	**11**
6	**12**

Boxes

Number of Players: two or more

Materials: a sheet of paper, pencils, articulation cards

Object of the Game: to put your initial in the most boxes

Articulation Practice

- Before the game, have the players say the words on all the cards.
- Have each player say the word on a card before connecting two dots.

Preparation: Draw rows and columns of dots on a sheet of paper. Make the grid as big as your playing time will allow. Give each player a pencil and place the stack of articulation cards facedown on the table.

To Play:

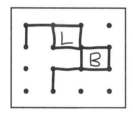

Choose a player to go first. This player turns over the top card, says the word on the card, and draws a line between two dots. The next player does the same. Players can connect any two dots across or down, but not diagonally. Players take turns until one of them completes a box. When a player completes a box, she puts her initials inside and takes another turn. When all the dots have been connected, count up the number of boxes per player. The player with the most boxes is the winner.

Variations: If a player says the word on a card correctly, she keeps the card. The winner is the one who has the most cards once all the dots have been connected. Players don't put their initials in the boxes as they complete them, but they do get another turn and a chance to earn another card. For articulation practice after the game, have the players say the words on the cards that they collect.

Triangles: Make a triangular grid of dots. Instead of making boxes, players connect the dots to make triangles.

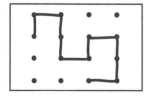

Snakes: Instead of making boxes, players make a continuous line that "snakes" back and forth inside the grid. The goal is to avoid connecting the line back to itself. On each turn, the player can connect either end of the continuous line to a dot above, below, or across from it (never diagonally). The player who makes the snake "bite" itself loses the game.

Bugs

Number of Players: two or more

Materials: one die, a sheet of paper for each player, a pencil or crayon for each player, articulation cards

Object of the Game: to be the first to draw a bug (Encourage creativity!)

Articulation Practice

- Before the game, have the players say the words on all the cards.
- Before throwing the die, have the player say the word on a card.
- After the game, have each player pass his cards to his left. Then have each player say the words on the new cards.

Preparation: Give each player a sheet of paper and a crayon or pencil. Place a set of articulation cards facedown on the table.

To Play: Choose a player to go first. This player turns over the top articulation card and says the word on the card. If he is correct, he keeps the card and throws the die. If he is incorrect, play passes to the next player. On each turn, a player draws the part of the bug that corresponds to the number on the die. See the chart below. The first player to complete a bug is the winner.

> 1=body
> 2=head
> 3=one leg
> 4=one eye
> 5=one antenna
> 6=tail

A complete bug is 1 head, 1 body, 2 eyes, 2 antennae, 6 legs, and 1 tail.

Note: A player must throw a 1 (body) to start and a 2 (head) before he can draw an eye or an antenna.

Variations: For a faster game, use two dice. The player can use either number on the dice or add the numbers together to match a body part he still needs to draw to win. For example, if he rolls a 1 and a 2, he can use the 1 and draw the body or add the 1 and 2 to draw a leg if he already has the body. Players can only draw one body part per turn.

For extra fun, allow the player to draw whatever part he rolls on the dice ignoring the rule to get a 1 or 2 first. Many players will find it a challenge to draw a leg before drawing the body—resulting in some really crazy-looking bugs!

 # Crazy Eights

Number of Players: two to five

Materials: four color-coded copies of any sound grid

Object of the Game: be the first player to get rid of all of your cards

Articulation Practice

- Have the player say the word on the card or use the word on the card in a sentence each time she plays one.

- Have players practice the words on all of their cards before playing the game.

- Have a player say eight words/sentences with her target sound any time she plays an (eight) 8.

- After the game, turn the cards in the discard pile over one at a time for players to take turns saying.

Preparation: If more than two players, deal five cards facedown to each player. If only two players, deal seven cards facedown to each player. Place the remaining cards facedown in a pile in the center. This is called the *stockpile*. Turn the top card faceup beside the stockpile. If the top card is an 8, return it to the stockpile (mix it in with the other cards in the stockpile) and turn over the next card.

To Play: Each player looks at the cards in her hand. The player to the left of the dealer goes first. She begins by laying a card from her hand onto the starter card that matches either by suit or denomination. For example, if the starter card is a red 6, the first player can play any other red card or a 6.

In this game, 8s are wild. A player can play an 8 at any time. When a player lays down an 8, she names a new color (red, blue, yellow, green). The following player must then play a card with the new color or an 8.

If the player cannot play a card, she takes cards from the stockpile until she gets a card she can play. (You may want to put a limit of three cards drawn from the stockpile to keep the game moving.) If the stockpile is gone, the player passes.

Play continues until a player has played her last card or until the stockpile is gone and no one can play any more cards.

Crazy Eights, *continued*

Variation: *Go Boom!:* This game is played much like *Crazy Eights*, but there are no wild cards and you take tricks.

Deal seven cards facedown to each person. The remaining cards are placed facedown in a pile in the center. The player to the left of the dealer goes first, playing any card she chooses. Each player then plays a card that matches either the color or the denomination of the card led. For example, if the starter card is a green 9, players may play any other green card or any 9.

The highest card of the color led wins the trick. If there is more than one card with the same denomination (e.g., two 9s), the first one played wins. The winner of the trick plays the first card of the next round.

If a player does not have a card with the correct color or denomination, she draws from the stockpile until she gets a card she can play. (You may want to put a limit of 3 cards drawn from the stockpile to keep the game moving.) If the stockpile is gone, the player passes.

Play continues until one player has played her last card. When a player plays her last card, she calls out "Boom!" The winner is the first person to get rid of all of her cards.

For articulation practice, have the winner of each trick say the words on the cards she wins in the trick. You can also have players practice the words on the cards they hold in their hands at the end of the game.

Fan Tan (also known as *7-Up*)

Number of Players: three to six

Materials: four copies of any sound grid (aces low; kings high)

Object of the Game: to get rid of all your cards

Articulation Practice

- Have the players say the words on all the cards in the deck before dealing.

- Have each player say the word on each card (or use it in a sentence) he lays down.

- Have each player say the word the same number of times as the rank (e.g., 10 times for a 10, 11 for a jack, 12 for a queen, and 13 for a king).

- At the end of each hand, have the players who are still holding cards say the word on each of the cards or use the words in sentences.

Preparation: Dealer deals the entire deck. Unless there are four players, some players will have more cards than others. As the deal rotates clockwise, this "inequity" will even out in future hands.

To Play: A player can only play a 7 or build up or down on cards already played, according to the suit. The player on the dealer's left begins and places a 7 faceup in the center of the table. If the player doesn't have a 7, he passes to the next player on his left. Once a 7 is played, a card higher or lower can be played (on the top half or lower half of the 7 respectively) in the same suit. Each player only plays one card at a time.

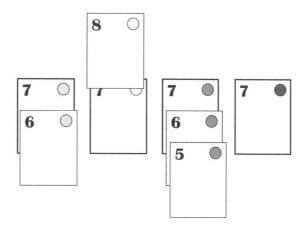

The first player to run out of cards is the winner.

For a shorter game, allow players to play straights (several cards in order of the same suit) or multiples (cards on more than one suit) on the same turn.

Variation: *Crazy Tan*: This game is a combination of *Crazy Eights* and *Fan Tan*. It is fun if you have a small group of two or three players. To play, the dealer deals seven cards to each player and places the rest of the deck facedown in the middle of the table as a stockpile. The game is played like *Fan Tan*, except when a player cannot play, he draws a card. If that card is playable, he plays it on this turn. Play then passes to the left as usual and continues until a player runs out of cards and is declared the winner.

To speed this game up, play with incremental drawing. For example, the first player to draw draws one card. If the next player doesn't have any playable cards, he draws two cards. If the next player can't play either, she draws three cards, and so on until one of the players is able to play. As soon as a card is played, the number of cards to draw goes back to one and the sequence repeats.

 # Go Fish

Number of Players: two to five

Materials: two copies of any sound grid

Object of the Game: to be the first player to get rid of all your cards

Articulation Practice

- Have the players practice the words on the cards before dealing.

- On each turn, have the player say the word on the card or use the word in the question, Do you have a _____?.

- At the end of the game, have the players who still have cards in their hands say the word on each of the cards or use them in sentences.

- After the game, turn the cards in the discard pile over one at a time for players to take turns saying.

Preparation: Deal all the cards facedown to the players, one hand for each player plus an extra. Place the extra hand in the center of the table. This is the *Go Fish* pond. If any of the players holds one or more pairs of cards, he places them faceup on the table in front of him.

To Play: The player to the left of the dealer goes first. He asks any player for a specific picture card (e.g., Mia, do you have a _____?). If the player has the requested card, she must hand it over. Player one then places the pair of cards on the table and continues his turn by asking any player for another card. If this player doesn't have the requested card, she says, "Go fish." Player one then draws a card from the *Go Fish* pond. If that card is the one requested (i.e., He fished what he wished), he lays the pair down and continues his turn. If not, play passes to the player who said, "Go fish."

If the *Go Fish* pond runs out of cards, play continues the same except that no one draws a card when told to "Go fish."

The first player to get rid of all his cards by laying down pairs is the winner.

Variation: Make four copies of the cards and lay down sets of four cards. With this variation, players ask, "Do you have any _____?" and the other player must surrender all matching cards.

# Memory (also known as *Concentration*)

Number of Players:	two to five
Materials:	two copies of any sound grid
Object of the Game:	to collect cards by matching pairs

Articulation Practice

- Have players practice the words on the cards before playing the game.

- Have the player say the word on the card or use the word on the card in a sentence each time she turns one over.

- At the end of the game, have players name each card they correctly matched.

Preparation: Mix up the cards and spread them out randomly facedown in front of all the players. Make sure no cards are overlapping.

To Play: Players take turns turning over two cards, looking for a match. If the cards match, the player takes another turn. If the cards do not match, the player turns the cards facedown in exactly the same spot and play passes to the left. Players try to remember where the cards are so they can make matches.

Play ends when all of the cards are matched. The player with the most pairs wins.

 # Michigan

Number of Players: three to eight

Materials: four color-coded copies of any sound grid sheet, the sheet of pay cards on page 68, 20 counters (e.g., poker chips, pennies) per player

Object of the Game: to be the first player to get rid of all of your cards

Articulation Practice

- Have players practice the words on the cards in their hands before playing the game.

- Have the player say the word on the card or use the word on the card in a sentence each time he plays one in a sequence.

- Whenever a player wins the counters from a pay card, have him count the counters and then practice words/sentences that many times (e.g., If he wins 6 counters, he says six words or uses six words in a sentence).

Preparation: Copy the sheet with the pay cards on page 68 and place it in the center of the table. (The pay cards are an ace, king, queen, and jack.) Give each player 20 counters. Before the deal, each player antes one counter on each pay card. The dealer then shuffles the cards and deals one hand to each player and one spare hand. All of the cards are dealt facedown, one at a time. (The deal may not come out evenly, but it doesn't matter.) The spare hand is left facedown and is not used in the game.

To Play: Each player looks at his hand. The person to the left of the dealer plays the lowest card he has in any color and names it out loud (e.g., "yellow 3"). The person with the next card in sequence with that color plays it and names the card (e.g., "yellow 4"). Then the player with the yellow 5 lays down her card and so on until either the ace is reached or no one can play because no one holds the next higher card in the sequence. (It might have been played earlier or it is in the spare hand.) At that point, the person who played last chooses a new color and plays her lowest card with that color.

Whenever a player lays down a pay card, she wins the counters on that pay card. If she forgets to collect her counters before the next player plays a card, she forfeits the counters.

When the cards are all played out, the hand is over. The deal passes to the left, the cards are shuffled, everyone antes, and a new hand is

dealt. Play continues until one player is bankrupt (in which case, he loses and everyone else wins) or until one player gets rid of all of his cards (in which case, he wins).

Pay Cards

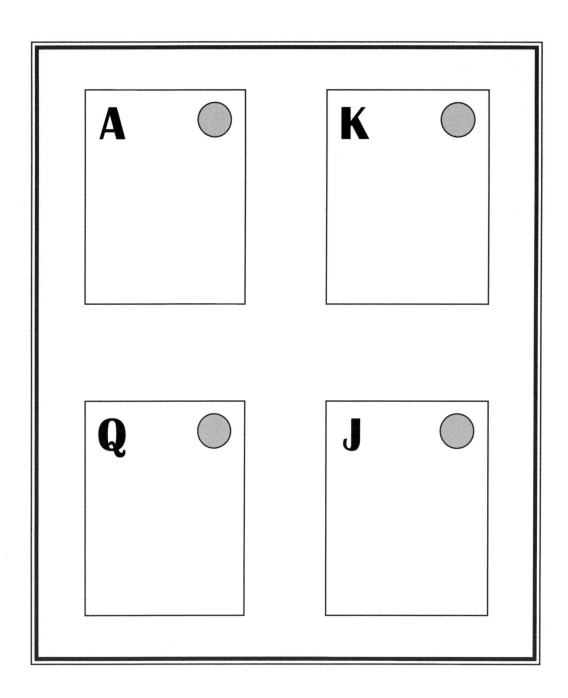

 **Oops!**

Number of Players: two or more

Materials: copies of one or more sound grids, the sheet of Oops! cards
on page 70

Object of the Game: to win the most cards

Articulation Practice

- Before the game, have the players say the words on all the cards.

- If the player is at the word level, have her say the word on the card a number of times for each turn. (You might set a certain number, or roll a die to determine the number each time.)

- If the player is at the sentence level, have her use the word on the card in a phrase/sentence.

Preparation: Put articulation cards in a box or bag along with the three Oops! cards (page 70).

To Play: Have students take turns pulling out a card and saying the word on the card. They keep the cards that they say correctly. If they get an Oops! card, they say "Oops!" and put all of their cards except the Oops! card back in the box or bag. Play continues until all of the articulation cards are out of the bag.

The player with the most cards is the winner.

Variation: Add any or all of the other cards on page 70 to the cards in the bag. Have students do what the card says like "Practice the words on all of your cards."

Oops!	Oops!	Oops!	
Practice the words on all of your cards.	Choose a card from your stack. Say it in a sentence.	Choose a card from your stack. Say it 5 times.	Practice the words on all of another student's cards.

Pay Up! (also called *Beggar My Neighbor* or *Beat Your Neighbor Out of Doors*)

Number of Players: two

Materials: four copies of any sound grid

Object of the Game: to win all the cards in the deck

Articulation Practice

- Have the players say the words on all the cards in the deck before dealing.

- On each turn, have the player say the word on the card (or use it in a sentence) as he lays down the card.

- Have the players say the words on the cards they take in each trick and/or the cards they take each time they win a 'pay.'

Preparation: Deal all the cards facedown to the players. Each player stacks his cards in a pile in front of him (without looking at them) and keeps the cards facedown.

To Play: The player who did not deal goes first. He turns over his top card in the center of the table. If it is a pay card (ace, king, queen, or jack), the other player must "pay" accordingly:

ace—four cards   queen—two cards
king—three cards   jack—one card

To pay, the player lays the appropriate number of cards faceup on the pay card. If in paying, she turns up another pay card, the original pay card is immediately canceled and the other player must now pay. This can continue as long as a pay card is turned up. Once payment is complete, the player who laid down the most recent pay card picks up the entire pile and places it under his stack of cards.

If the first card is not a pay card, the other player turns over her top card and places it on top of the other card in the middle of the table. Players take turns playing a card face up in the middle until a pay card is played.

The first player to win all the cards in the deck is the winner. If a player runs out of cards in the middle of a payment, he forfeits the cards and the other player is declared the winner.

Variation: To shorten the game, set a time limit. At the end of the time period, the player with the most cards is the winner.

# Play or Pay

Number of Players: three to five

Materials: four color-coded copies of any sound grid sheet, 20 counters (e.g., poker chips, pennies) per player

Object of the Game: to be the first player to get rid of all of your cards
to have the most counters after a set number of hands (or to reach a predetermined number of counters first)

Articulation Practice

- Have players practice the words on the cards in their hands before playing the game.

- Have the player say the word on the card or use the word on the card in a sentence each time she plays one in a sequence.

- When a person finishes a sequence, have her practice all of the words on the cards in that sequence.

- At the end of each game, have the "losers" practice the words on the cards they hold in their hands.

Preparation: Give each player 20 counters. Deal all the cards facedown to the players. The deal may not come out evenly.

To Play: The player to the left of the dealer chooses a card from her hand and puts it faceup in the center of the playing area. The person to her left puts down the next card in the sequence (e.g., blue 4, blue 5). If that player does not have the next card in the sequence, he "pays" one of his counters into the middle of the playing area. The player to his left then takes a turn.

If the first player doesn't start with an ace, and the sequence gets to a king, the next card in the sequence is the ace, then the two (2), etc. When a whole sequence is finished, the person who plays the last card in the sequence puts down a new card in the middle to begin a new sequence.

Players continue to play or "pay" until one player runs out of cards. The player who runs out of cards first wins all the counters in the middle as well as a counter for each card each opponent holds (e.g., A player with three cards left pays the winner three counters). The winner is the player who has the most counters after a set number of hands or who reaches a predetermined number first (e.g., 50 counters).

Red Out (also called *Hearts*)

Number of Players: three to six

Materials: four color-coded copies of any sound grid (aces high)

Object of the Game: to get the lowest score
to get rid of your red cards

Articulation Practice

- Have the players say the words on all the cards in the deck before dealing.

- On each turn, have the player say the word on the card (or use it in a sentence) as he lays down the card.

- Have the players say the words on the cards they take in each trick.

- At the end of each round, have each player say the words on all his cards.

Preparation: Choose a dealer and a scorekeeper. The dealer deals the cards evenly. In a four-player game, each player gets 13 cards. In games with numbers other than four players, remove card(s) as follows to make the deal come out evenly.

# Players	Discard
3	blue 2
4	none
5	blue 2, green 2
6	blue 2, green 2, yellow 2

To Play: *Red Out* is played as a series of hands and points are tallied after each hand. The player with the blue 2 (or lowest blue card) plays first. Play proceeds clockwise, each player playing a blue card if possible. If a player doesn't have a blue card, he may play any card. Usually a player in this situation would play a red card to get rid of point cards. No one can lead with a red card until a red card has been played as a discard. The player who plays the highest card in the initially led suit wins the trick. This player leads the next round. Play continues until all players are out of cards. At the end of each hand, the scorekeeper records the points for each player according to the number of red cards taken in tricks (one point per red card).

The player with the lowest point total when another player reaches 50 points is the winner.

**Red Out**, *continued*

Variations:

To shorten the game: Set a time limit. At the end of the time period, the player with the lowest score is declared the winner.

Yellow Queen: All red cards and the yellow queen are penalty cards. The player who takes the yellow queen in a round receives 13 points. Each red card is still worth 1 point. Play continues until a player reaches 100 points or the time limit ends. The winner is the player with the lowest score.

Shoot the Moon: If a player takes all the red cards and the yellow queen, he gets 0 points for the hand, but every other player gets 26 points. Play continues until a player reaches 100 points or the time limit ends. The winner is the player with the lowest score.

Spot Hearts: Points are awarded based on the rank of the red card. For example, if a player takes the red 10, he gets 10 points added to his score. The king counts 13, the queen 12, and the jack 11. The winner is the player with the lowest score.

Passing Red Out: This is a game for four players. After each deal, each player selects three cards from his hand and passes them to another player facedown. Players must select and pass their cards before they pick up the cards passed to them. The direction they pass their cards depends on the hand. On the first hand they pass to the left, on the second hand to the right, on the third hand across the table, and on the fourth hand they don't pass any cards. The passing sequence resumes for the fifth hand and so on. Play continues until a player reaches 100 points or the time limit ends. The winner is the player with the lowest score.

Domino Red Out: The dealer deals 6 cards to each player and places the rest of the cards in the middle of the table facedown. If a player cannot follow suit, he draws cards from the stock until he gets the necessary suit. Once the stock cards are depleted, play reverts to the regular Red Out play. Players drop out as they run out of cards and the last player with cards in his hands scores points for red cards in his hand as well as taken in tricks. All the other players score points normally. The winner is the player with the least points when another player reaches 31 points.

Solitaire

Number of Players: one or two

Materials: four color-coded copies of any sound grid

Object of the Game: to move the four aces, as they appear, to the foundation piles
to build on the aces in the foundation piles going from ace to king

Articulation Practice

- Have players practice the words on the cards before playing the game.

- Have the player say the word on the card or use the word on the card in a sentence each time she turns one over.

- Each time a player moves a card, have her practice the word on the card.

- At the end of the game, have players practice the words in the foundation piles.

Preparation: Lay out the cards in seven columns, with the first column containing one card, the second column two cards, etc. The top card in each column is faceup and the remainder of the cards are facedown. Place the rest of the deck facedown in front of the player to form the stockpile.

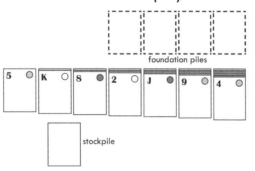

To Play: Have the player turn one card at a time faceup from the stockpile. If the card is an ace, it goes above the columns as one of the foundation piles. If the card is not an ace, it may be played on the foundations (e.g., a red 10 on a red 9) or on the cards in the columns (e.g., a red 10 on a yellow jack). The card turned up may not be playable. In that case, it goes facedown on the wastepile. If you play with two players, have them take turns turning over cards.

Cards in the columns may be built down in sequence and in different colors (e.g., red 8, green 7, yellow 6, red 5).

A sequence of cards (or one card) can be moved as a unit from one pile to another. When a facedown card is exposed as a result of moving a sequence of cards, turn it faceup. That card may then be

playable on a foundation pile or on another column. If a space is created in a column as a result of moving a sequence of cards, it may only be filled with a king.

The stockpile can be reused as many times as necessary. Play continues until the player fills all foundations (in which case, she won) or when no more moves are possible (in which case, she lost).

Variation:

Clock Solitaire: Put 13 cards facedown in a circle, with one card representing each number on a clock (e.g., one card at the one o'clock spot, another card at the two o'clock spot, etc.). The 13th card goes facedown in the center. Go around the circle three more times, placing cards facedown to create 13 piles of four cards each. In this game, the face value of the card represents a time on the clock (e.g., aces represent one o'clock, jacks represent 11 o'clock).

Have the player take the top card off the pile in the center of the circle and place the card faceup under the pile of cards representing the "time" on the card (e.g., queen = 12 o'clock). Then the player takes the top facedown card off that pile and plays it the same way. If two players are playing, have them take turns turning over cards.

Play continues until the player gets all four kings (in which case, she lost) or when all piles of cards have all four colors and a king is the last card (in which case, she won).

For articulation practice, the player can say the word on the card (or use it in a sentence) each time she turns one faceup. At the end of the game, have the player name all of the cards around the "clock."

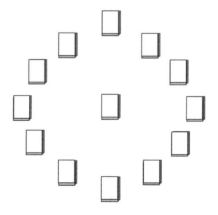

 # Tic-Tac-Toe

Number of Players: two

Materials: paper, pencils, nine articulation cards, two different groups of five tokens (e.g., coins, poker chips)

Object of the Game: get three across, down, or diagonally

Articulation Practice

- Before the game, have the players say the words on all the cards.

- On each turn, have the player say the word on the card before he covers it with a token.

- After the game, have each player say the word on each card as he takes off the other player's tokens.

Preparation: Select nine articulation cards and lay them out in a 3 X 3 grid. Give each player five tokens, choosing them so one player's tokens can be distinguished from the other player's tokens.

To Play: Choose a player to go first. This player says the word on a card and covers it with a token. The other player does the same. A player can place his token so that the other player is blocked from getting three in a row. Play continues until a player has covered three cards across, down, or diagonally.

Variations: If a player misarticulates his target sound, he doesn't place a token on the card and play passes to the other player.

If a player misarticulates his target sound, the other player has a chance to say the word correctly and place his token on that card. Then it is the first player's turn again.

War

Number of Players: two

Materials: four copies of any sound grid

Object of the Game: to win all the cards in the deck

Articulation Practice

- Have the players practice all the words in the deck of cards before dealing.

- On each turn, have the player say the word on the card (or use it in a sentence) as she lays down the card.

- Have the players say the words on the cards they take in each trick.

- When a player wins a "war," have her say the words on all the cards she takes in.

Preparation: Deal all the cards facedown to the players. Each player stacks her cards in a pile in front of her (without looking at them) and keeps the cards facedown.

To Play: Each player turns over the top card of her stack of cards, names it, and places it in the middle of the table. The player with the higher card takes both cards and places them in a discard pile beside her. (Aces are high.) Whenever a player runs out of cards, she takes her discard pile (without shuffling them or looking at them) and continues play by turning over the top card. Players continue flipping over their top cards, naming them, and taking tricks until they both turn over a card with the same rank (e.g., 2 queens). Then it's war. At the same time, players place their top two cards facedown and the third card faceup in front of them. To add drama, they can chant "1, 2, 3!" as they turn over their cards. Whoever has the highest faceup card, takes all of the cards in that round (the two original cards, the four facedown cards and the final two faceup cards). This sequence is repeated if the new faceup cards are also the same rank.

The first player to win all the cards in the deck is the winner. If a player doesn't have enough cards to finish a round of war, she must surrender her cards to the other player and he wins by default.

Note: This game can take a long time, so you may want to set a time limit. At the end of the time period, the player with the most cards is declared the winner.

Variations: There are other ways to play when players get a "war":

1. Each player puts one card facedown and one card faceup.
2. Each player puts three cards facedown and one card faceup.
3. The number of cards placed facedown depends on the rank of
    the faceup cards that caused the war (e.g., Players put five cards
    facedown for a 5, 11 for a jack).

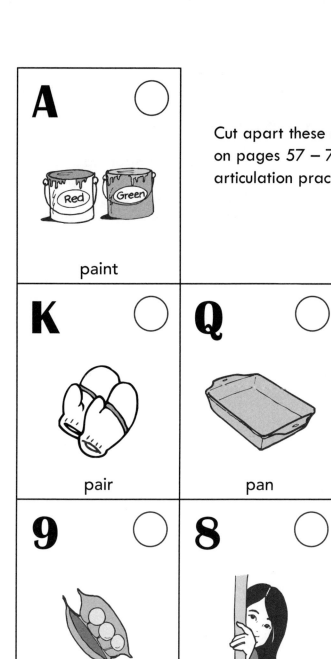

A ◯

paint

Cut apart these cards to use with the card games suggested on pages 57 – 79. You can also use this page as is for articulation practice.

K ◯

pair

Q ◯

pan

J ◯

pants

10 ◯

path

9 ◯

peas

8 ◯

peek

7 ◯

peel

6 ◯

pen

5 ◯

pie

4 ◯

pig

3 ◯

pin

2 ◯

pool

initial /p/ — 1 syllable
50 Quick-Play Articulation Games

80

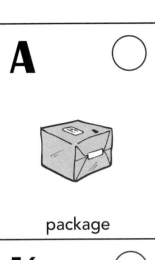

A ◯

package

Cut apart these cards to use with the card games suggested on pages 57 – 79. You can also use this page as is for articulation practice.

K ◯	**Q** ◯	**J** ◯	**10** ◯
pajamas	pancakes	pencil	penny
9 ◯	**8** ◯	**7** ◯	**6** ◯
petal	piano	pillow	pilot
5 ◯	**4** ◯	**3** ◯	**2** ◯
pizza	police officer	pony	puzzle

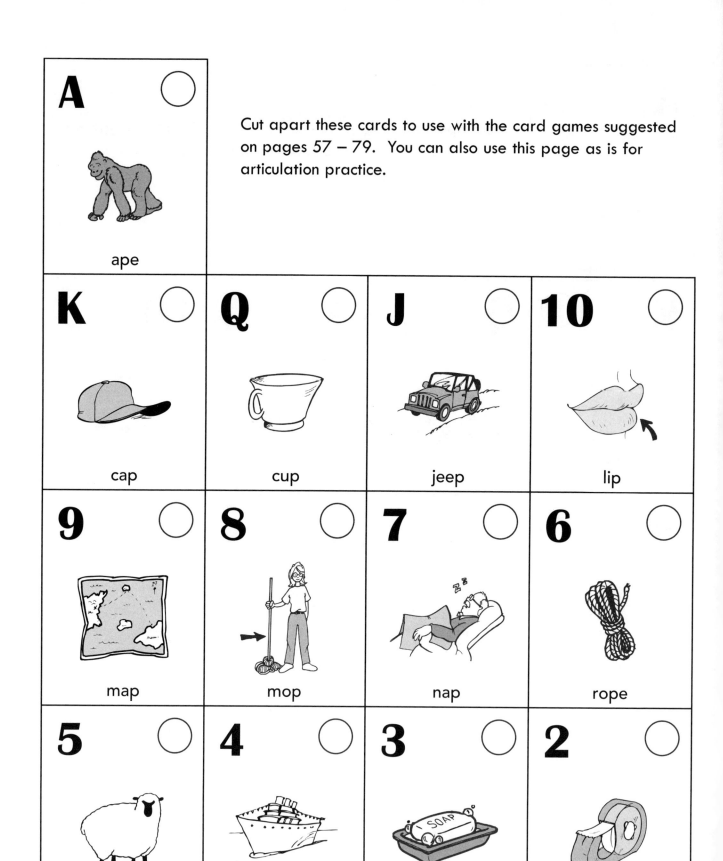

A ◯

ape

Cut apart these cards to use with the card games suggested on pages 57 – 79. You can also use this page as is for articulation practice.

K ◯

cap

Q ◯

cup

J ◯

jeep

10 ◯

lip

9 ◯

map

8 ◯

mop

7 ◯

nap

6 ◯

rope

5 ◯

sheep

4 ◯

ship

3 ◯

soap

2 ◯

tape

final /p/ — 1 syllable
50 Quick-Play Articulation Games

82

A ◯

bus stop

Cut apart these cards to use with the card games suggested on pages 57 – 79. You can also use this page as is for articulation practice.

K ◯

envelope

Q ◯

fingertip

J ◯

gallop

10 ◯

grown-up

9 ◯

ketchup

8 ◯

makeup

7 ◯

mousetrap

6 ◯

raindrop

5 ◯

syrup

4 ◯

telescope

3 ◯

tightrope

2 ◯

tulip

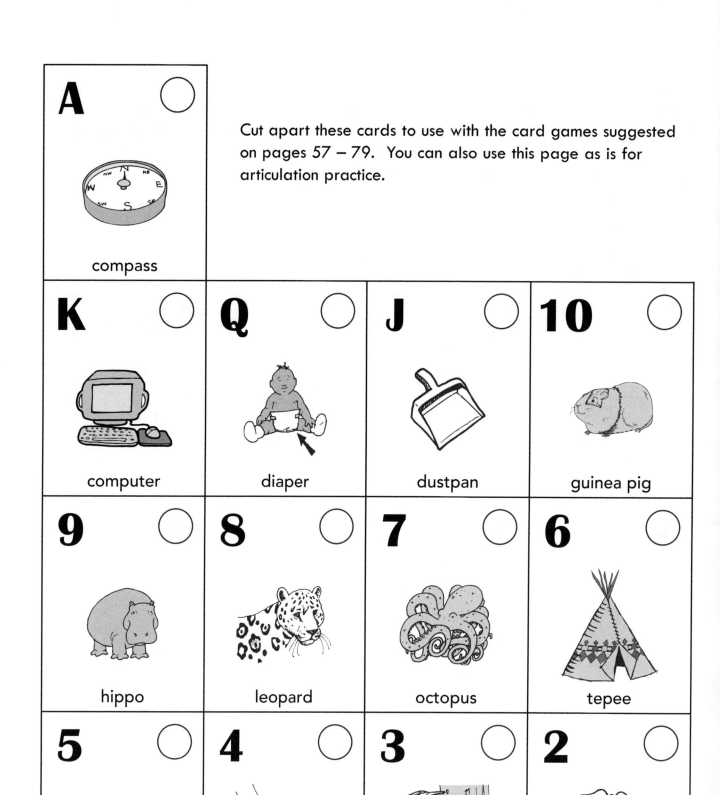

A ◯

compass

Cut apart these cards to use with the card games suggested on pages 57 – 79. You can also use this page as is for articulation practice.

K ◯

computer

Q ◯

diaper

J ◯

dustpan

10 ◯

guinea pig

9 ◯

hippo

8 ◯

leopard

7 ◯

octopus

6 ◯

tepee

5 ◯

toothpaste

4 ◯

trapeze

3 ◯

woodpecker

2 ◯

zipper

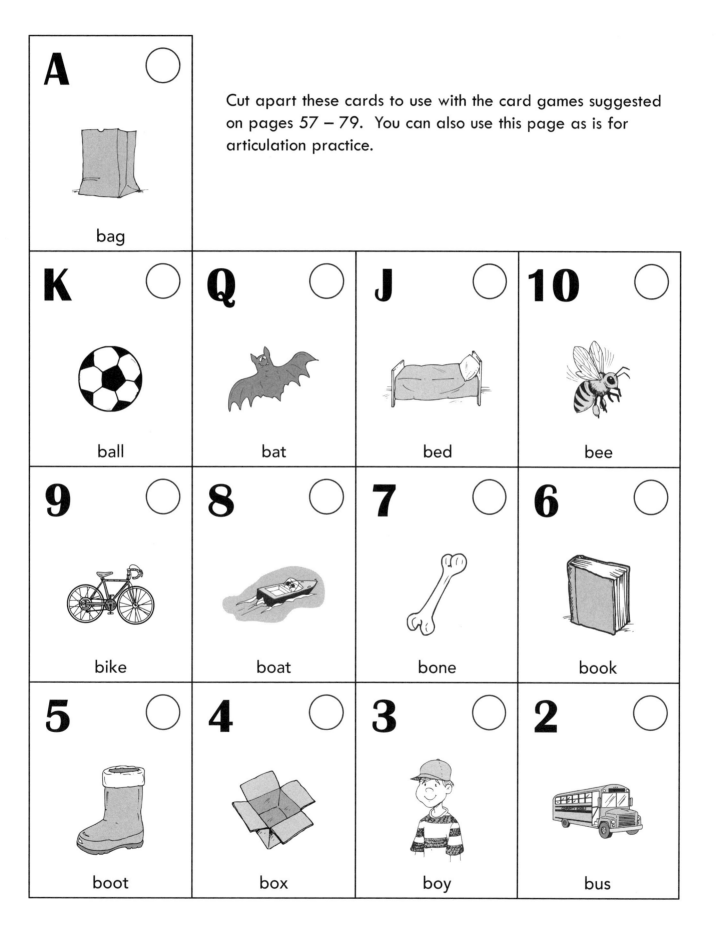

A ◯

bag

Cut apart these cards to use with the card games suggested on pages 57 – 79. You can also use this page as is for articulation practice.

K ◯

ball

Q ◯

bat

J ◯

bed

10 ◯

bee

9 ◯

bike

8 ◯

boat

7 ◯

bone

6 ◯

book

5 ◯

boot

4 ◯

box

3 ◯

boy

2 ◯

bus

initial /b/ — 1 syllable
50 Quick-Play Articulation Games

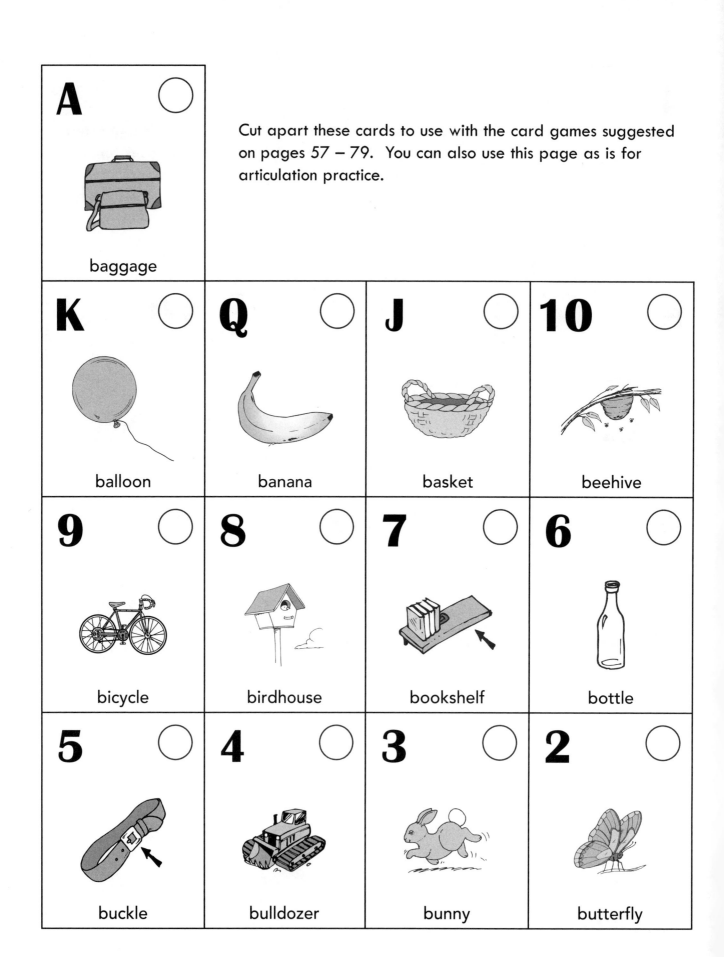

A ◯

baggage

Cut apart these cards to use with the card games suggested on pages 57 – 79. You can also use this page as is for articulation practice.

K ◯

balloon

Q ◯

banana

J ◯

basket

10 ◯

beehive

9 ◯

bicycle

8 ◯

birdhouse

7 ◯

bookshelf

6 ◯

bottle

5 ◯

buckle

4 ◯

bulldozer

3 ◯

bunny

2 ◯

butterfly

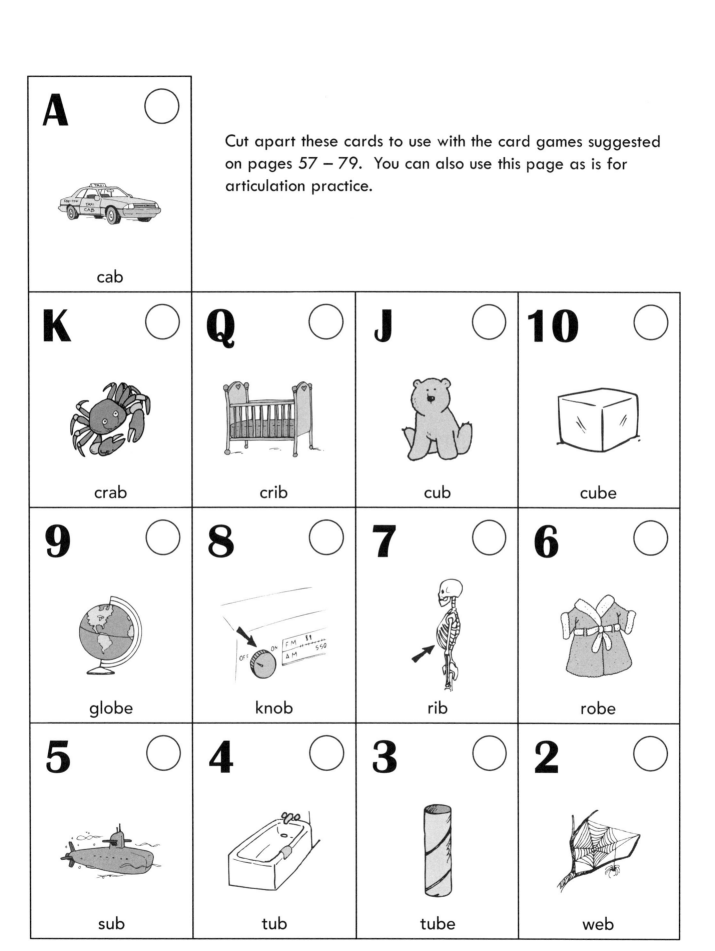

A ◯

cab

Cut apart these cards to use with the card games suggested on pages 57 – 79. You can also use this page as is for articulation practice.

K ◯

crab

Q ◯

crib

J ◯

cub

10 ◯

cube

9 ◯

globe

8 ◯

knob

7 ◯

rib

6 ◯

robe

5 ◯

sub

4 ◯

tub

3 ◯

tube

2 ◯

web

A ◯

corncob

Cut apart these cards to use with the card games suggested on pages 57 – 79. You can also use this page as is for articulation practice.

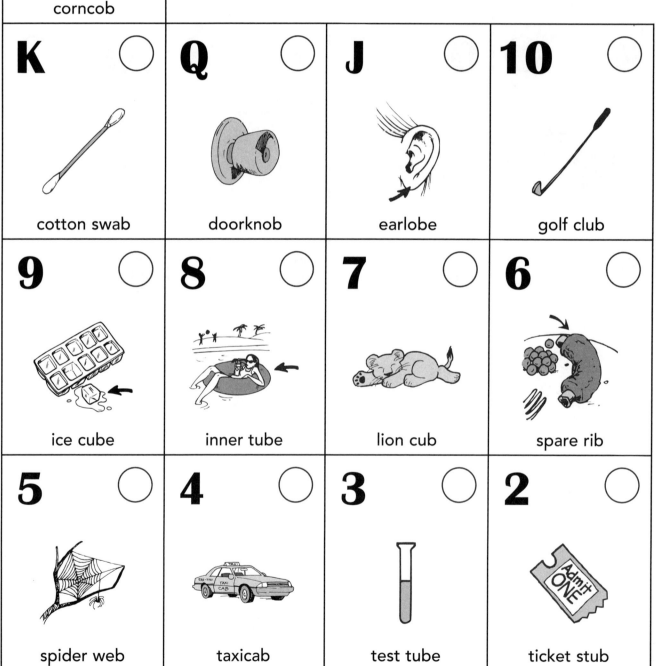

K ◯

cotton swab

Q ◯

doorknob

J ◯

earlobe

10 ◯

golf club

9 ◯

ice cube

8 ◯

inner tube

7 ◯

lion cub

6 ◯

spare rib

5 ◯

spider web

4 ◯

taxicab

3 ◯

test tube

2 ◯

ticket stub

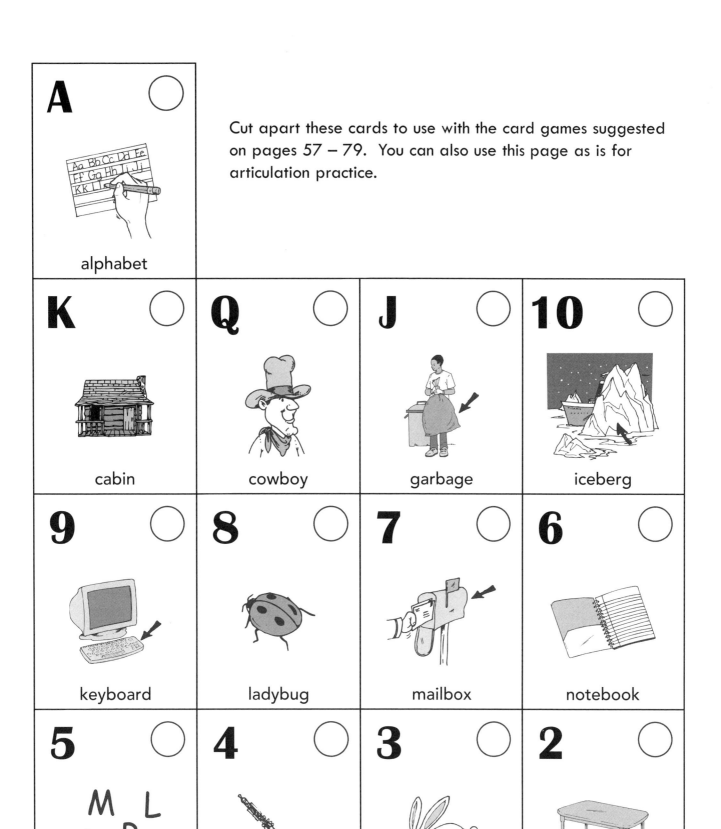

A ⊙

alphabet

Cut apart these cards to use with the card games suggested on pages 57 – 79. You can also use this page as is for articulation practice.

K ⊙

cabin

Q ⊙

cowboy

J ⊙

garbage

10 ⊙

iceberg

9 ⊙

keyboard

8 ⊙

ladybug

7 ⊙

mailbox

6 ⊙

notebook

5 ⊙

number

4 ⊙

oboe

3 ⊙

rabbit

2 ⊙

table

A ◯

man

Cut apart these cards to use with the card games suggested on pages 57 – 79. You can also use this page as is for articulation practice.

K ◯	**Q** ◯	**J** ◯	**10** ◯
mane	map	men	mice

9 ◯	**8** ◯	**7** ◯	**6** ◯
milk	mitt	moon	moose

5 ◯	**4** ◯	**3** ◯	**2** ◯
moth	mouse	mouth	mug

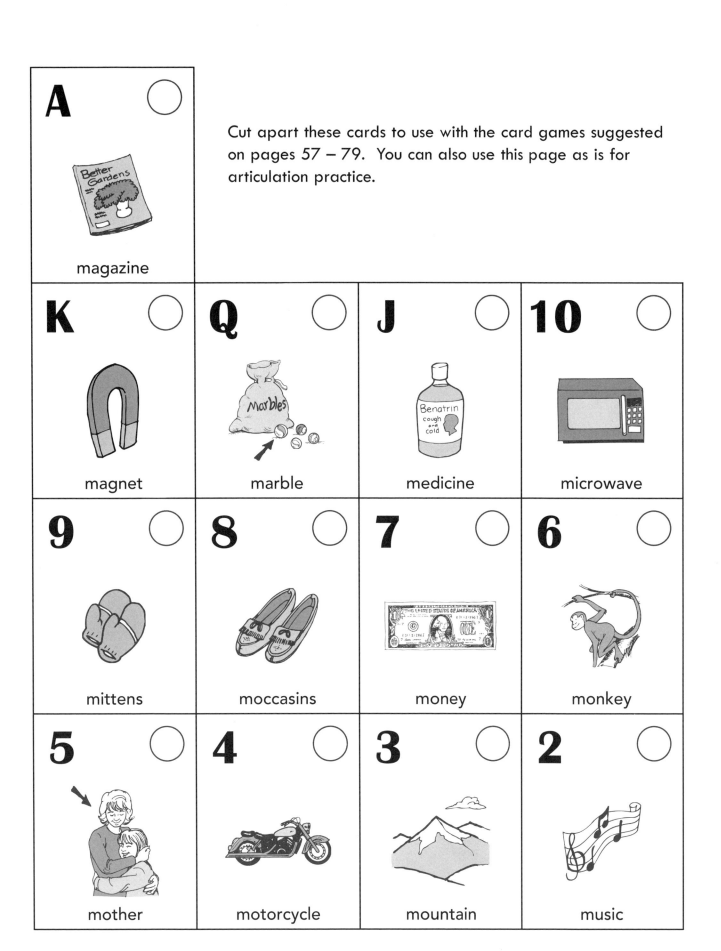

A ◯

magazine

Cut apart these cards to use with the card games suggested on pages 57 – 79. You can also use this page as is for articulation practice.

K ◯

magnet

Q ◯

marble

J ◯

medicine

10 ◯

microwave

9 ◯

mittens

8 ◯

moccasins

7 ◯

money

6 ◯

monkey

5 ◯

mother

4 ◯

motorcycle

3 ◯

mountain

2 ◯

music

initial /m/ — multisyllable
50 Quick-Play Articulation Games

A ◯

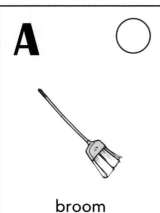

broom

Cut apart these cards to use with the card games suggested on pages 57 – 79. You can also use this page as is for articulation practice.

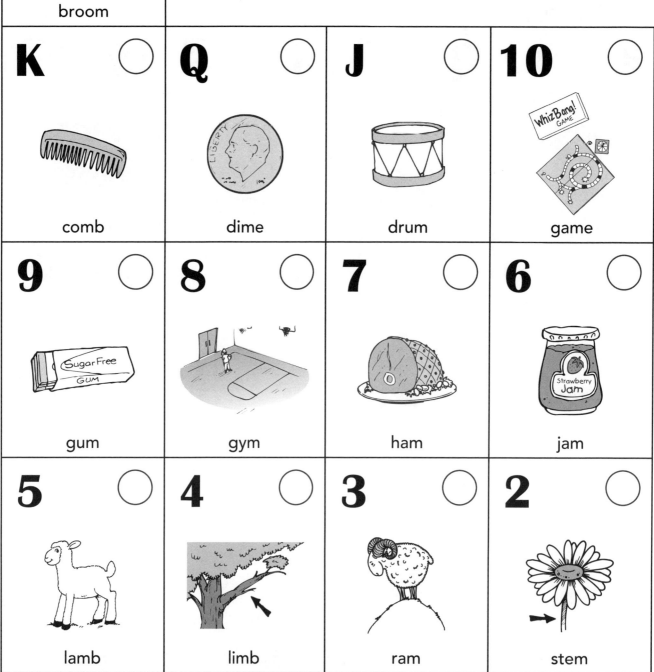

K ◯	**Q** ◯	**J** ◯	**10** ◯
comb	dime	drum	game
9 ◯	**8** ◯	**7** ◯	**6** ◯
gum	gym	ham	jam
5 ◯	**4** ◯	**3** ◯	**2** ◯
lamb	limb	ram	stem

A ◯

album

Cut apart these cards to use with the card games suggested on pages 57 – 79. You can also use this page as is for articulation practice.

K ◯	Q ◯	J ◯	10 ◯
autumn	bathroom	bedroom	blossom
9 ◯	**8** ◯	**7** ◯	**6** ◯
bottom	ice cream	opossum	pilgrim
5 ◯	**4** ◯	**3** ◯	**2** ◯
snowstorm	storeroom	wigwam	wind chime

A ◯

animals

Cut apart these cards to use with the card games suggested on pages 57 – 79. You can also use this page as is for articulation practice.

K ◯

camel

Q ◯

camera

J ◯

chimney

10 ◯

comet

9 ◯

dominoes

8 ◯

hammer

7 ◯

lemon

6 ◯

plumber

5 ◯

somersault

4 ◯

summer

3 ◯

tomato

2 ◯

women

A ◯

cage

Cut apart these cards to use with the card games suggested on pages 57 – 79. You can also use this page as is for articulation practice.

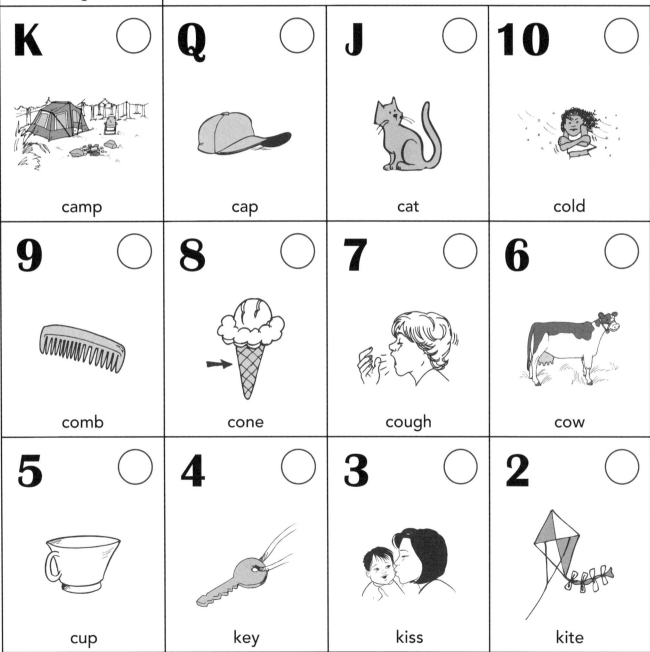

K ◯	**Q** ◯	**J** ◯	**10** ◯
camp	cap	cat	cold
9 ◯	**8** ◯	**7** ◯	**6** ◯
comb	cone	cough	cow
5 ◯	**4** ◯	**3** ◯	**2** ◯
cup	key	kiss	kite

A ◯

DECEMBER

calendar

Cut apart these cards to use with the card games suggested on pages 57 – 79. You can also use this page as is for articulation practice.

K ◯

camel

Q ◯

campfire

J ◯

canoe

10 ◯

caterpillar

9 ◯

cattle

8 ◯

color

7 ◯

comet

6 ◯

compass

5 ◯

computer

4 ◯

kangaroo

3 ◯

keyboard

2 ◯

kitten

A ◯

bike

Cut apart these cards to use with the card games suggested on pages 57 – 79. You can also use this page as is for articulation practice.

K ◯

book

Q ◯

check

J ◯

cheek

10 ◯

duck

9 ◯

hawk

8 ◯

hook

7 ◯

lake

6 ◯

neck

5 ◯

peek

4 ◯

rake

3 ◯

rock

2 ◯

sock

A ○

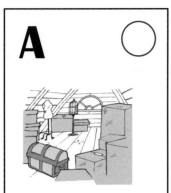

attic

Cut apart these cards to use with the card games suggested on pages 57 – 79. You can also use this page as is for articulation practice.

K ○	**Q** ○	**J** ○	**10** ○
earthquake	fire truck	hammock	haystack
9 ○	**8** ○	**7** ○	**6** ○
music	notebook	padlock	paperback
5 ○	**4** ○	**3** ○	**2** ○
railroad track	rattlesnake	snowflake	stomach

A ◯

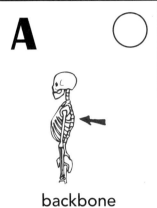

backbone

Cut apart these cards to use with the card games suggested on pages 57 – 79. You can also use this page as is for articulation practice.

K ◯	**Q** ◯	**J** ◯	**10** ◯
chicken	helicopter	macaroni	nickel
9 ◯	**8** ◯	**7** ◯	**6** ◯
package	pocket	pumpkin	raccoon
5 ◯	**4** ◯	**3** ◯	**2** ◯
second	soccer	taco	volcano

A ○

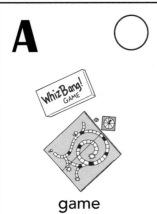

game

Cut apart these cards to use with the card games suggested on pages 57 – 79. You can also use this page as is for articulation practice.

K ○	**Q** ○	**J** ○	**10** ○
gate	geese	gift	girl
9 ○	**8** ○	**7** ○	**6** ○
give	go	goal	golf
5 ○	**4** ○	**3** ○	**2** ○
goose	gown	gull	gum

A ◯

gallon

Cut apart these cards to use with the card games suggested on pages 57 – 79. You can also use this page as is for articulation practice.

K ◯	**Q** ◯	**J** ◯	**10** ◯
gallop	game board	garage	garbage

9 ◯	**8** ◯	**7** ◯	**6** ◯
garden	garden hose	gasoline	geyser

5 ◯	**4** ◯	**3** ◯	**2** ◯
goldfish	good-bye	gorilla	guitar

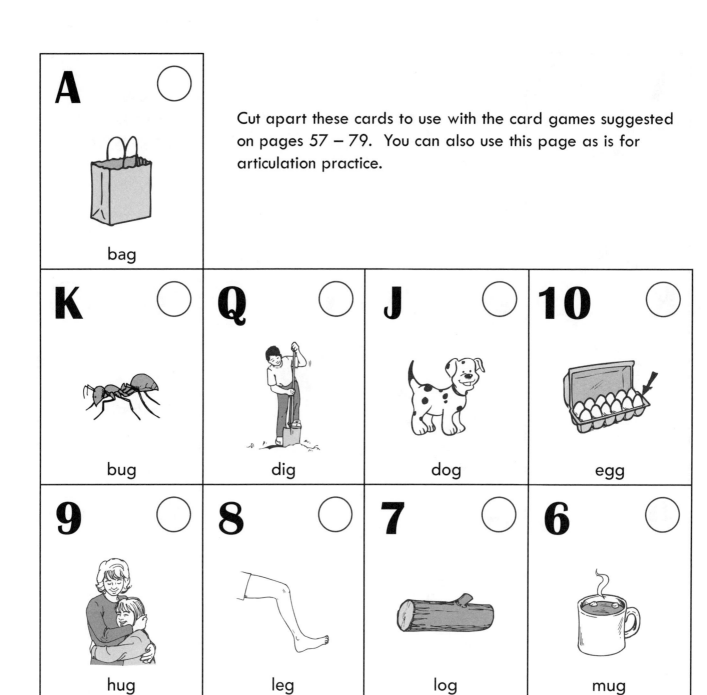

Cut apart these cards to use with the card games suggested on pages 57 – 79. You can also use this page as is for articulation practice.

A ○

bag

K ○

bug

Q ○

dig

J ○

dog

10 ○

egg

9 ○

hug

8 ○

leg

7 ○

log

6 ○

mug

5 ○

pig

4 ○

rag

3 ○

tag

2 ○

wag

final /g/ — 1 syllable
50 Quick-Play Articulation Games

A ◯

Cut apart these cards to use with the card games suggested on pages 57 – 79. You can also use this page as is for articulation practice.

bear hug

K ◯	**Q** ◯	**J** ◯	**10** ◯
bulldog	catalog	duffel bag	hedgehog
9 ◯	**8** ◯	**7** ◯	**6** ◯
hot dog	ladybug	litterbug	polliwog
5 ◯	**4** ◯	**3** ◯	**2** ◯
prairie dog	sleeping bag	tea bag	trash bag

A ◯

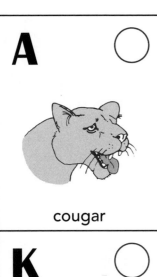

cougar

Cut apart these cards to use with the card games suggested on pages 57 – 79. You can also use this page as is for articulation practice.

K ◯	**Q** ◯	**J** ◯	**10** ◯
dragon	eagle	hamburger	kangaroo
9 ◯	**8** ◯	**7** ◯	**6** ◯
magnet	nightgown	rectangle	sea gull
5 ◯	**4** ◯	**3** ◯	**2** ◯
sugar	tiger	triangle	wagon

A ⚪

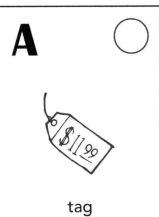

tag

Cut apart these cards to use with the card games suggested on pages 57 – 79. You can also use this page as is for articulation practice.

K ⚪	Q ⚪	J ⚪	10 ⚪
tail	tall	tape	tea

9 ⚪	8 ⚪	7 ⚪	6 ⚪
ten	tie	toe	toys

5 ⚪	4 ⚪	3 ⚪	2 ⚪
tub	tube	tug	two

A ⃝

table

Cut apart these cards to use with the card games suggested on pages 57 – 79. You can also use this page as is for articulation practice.

K ⃝ taco

Q ⃝ taxi

J ⃝ teacher

10 ⃝ teddy bear

9 ⃝ teenager

8 ⃝ telephone

7 ⃝ tennis

6 ⃝ tiger

5 ⃝ tissue

4 ⃝ towel

3 ⃝ tunnel

2 ⃝ TV

initial /t/ — multisyllable
50 Quick-Play Articulation Games

106

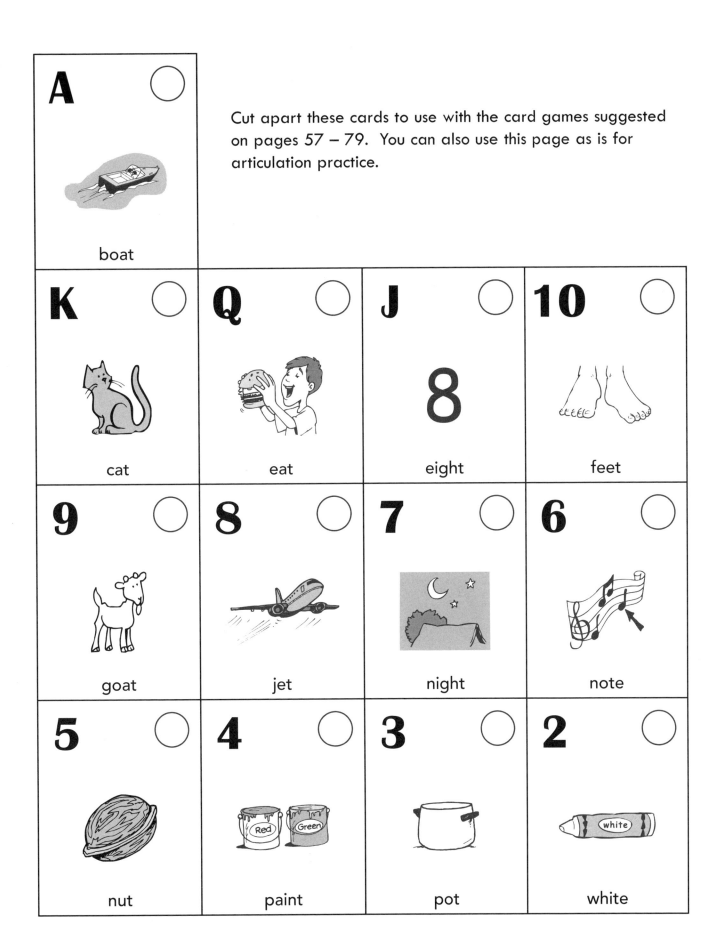

A ◯

boat

Cut apart these cards to use with the card games suggested on pages 57 – 79. You can also use this page as is for articulation practice.

K ◯

cat

Q ◯

eat

J ◯

8

eight

10 ◯

feet

9 ◯

goat

8 ◯

jet

7 ◯

night

6 ◯

note

5 ◯

nut

4 ◯

paint

3 ◯

pot

2 ◯

white

A ◯

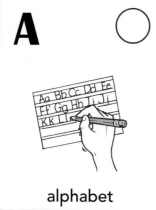

alphabet

Cut apart these cards to use with the card games suggested on pages 57 – 79. You can also use this page as is for articulation practice.

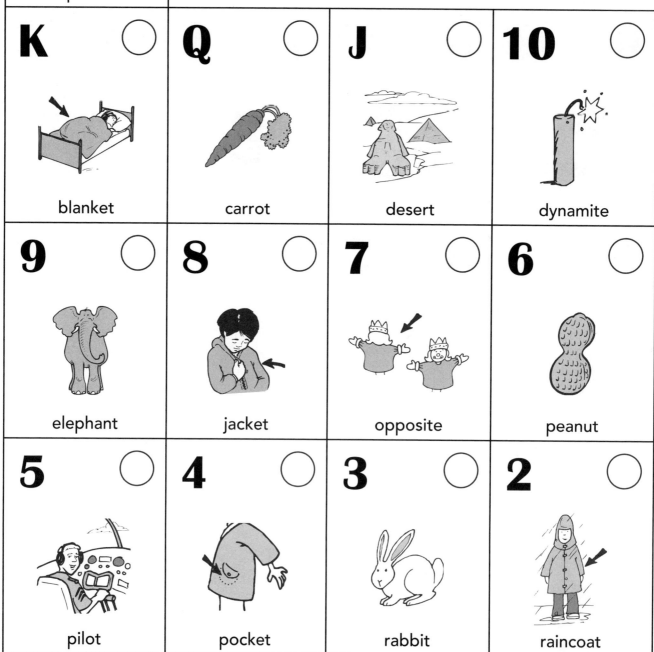

K ◯	**Q** ◯	**J** ◯	**10** ◯
blanket	carrot	desert	dynamite
9 ◯	**8** ◯	**7** ◯	**6** ◯
elephant	jacket	opposite	peanut
5 ◯	**4** ◯	**3** ◯	**2** ◯
pilot	pocket	rabbit	raincoat

A ◯

capitol

Cut apart these cards to use with the card games suggested on pages 57 – 79. You can also use this page as is for articulation practice.

K ◯

conductor

Q ◯

diameter

J ◯

empty

10 ◯

50

fifty

9 ◯

55

fifty-five

8 ◯

guitar

7 ◯

October

6 ◯

reptile

5 ◯

September

4 ◯

13

thirteen

3 ◯

valentine

2 ◯

videotape

A

dance

Cut apart these cards to use with the card games suggested on pages 57 – 79. You can also use this page as is for articulation practice.

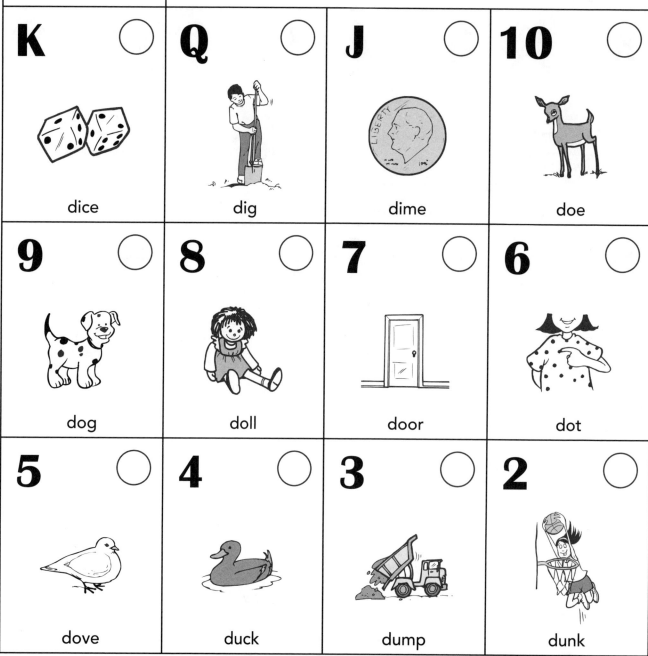

K	Q	J	10
dice	dig	dime	doe
9	**8**	**7**	**6**
dog	doll	door	dot
5	**4**	**3**	**2**
dove	duck	dump	dunk

A ○			
 daisy	Cut apart these cards to use with the card games suggested on pages 57 – 79. You can also use this page as is for articulation practice.		

K ○	**Q** ○	**J** ○	**10** ○
diaper	dictionary	different	dinner
9 ○	**8** ○	**7** ○	**6** ○
dinosaur	dishwasher	dollar	dollhouse
5 ○	**4** ○	**3** ○	**2** ○
dolphin	doorknob	doughnut	dozen

initial /d/ — multisyllable
50 Quick-Play Articulation Games

111

A ⃝

$2+4=6$

add

Cut apart these cards to use with the card games suggested on pages 57 – 79. You can also use this page as is for articulation practice.

K ⃝

bead

Q ⃝

hand

J ⃝

head

10 ⃝

hood

9 ⃝

pound

8 ⃝

ride

7 ⃝

road

6 ⃝

sad

5 ⃝

seed

4 ⃝

side

3 ⃝

toad

2 ⃝

wood

A ○
barnyard

Cut apart these cards to use with the card games suggested on pages 57 – 79. You can also use this page as is for articulation practice.

K ○
behind

Q ○
bunk bed

J ○
chalkboard

10 ○
cornfield

9 ○
firewood

8 ○
inside

7 ○
island

6 ○
lemonade

5 ○
neighborhood

4 ○
parade

3 ○
I went to the store.
period

2 ○
salad

final /d/ — multisyllable
50 Quick-Play Articulation Games

A ◯

$2+4=6$

addition

Cut apart these cards to use with the card games suggested on pages 57 – 79. You can also use this page as is for articulation practice.

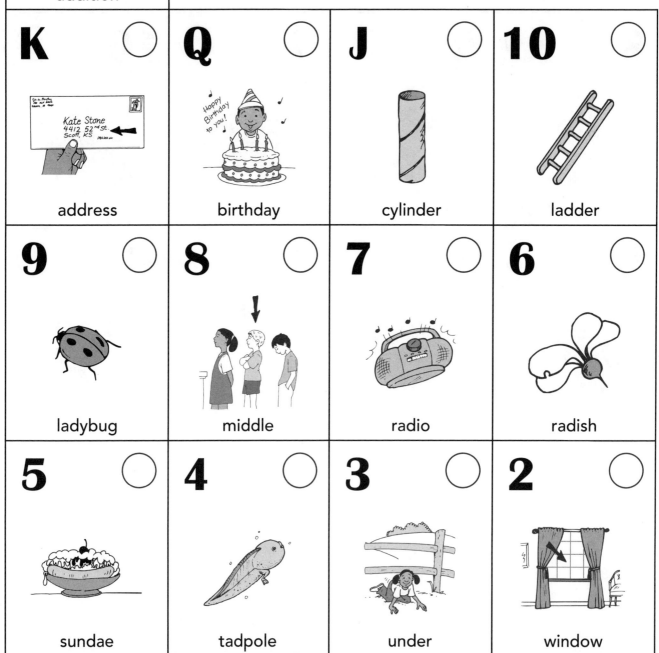

K ◯

Kate Stone
4412 52ⁿᵈ St.
Scott, KS

address

Q ◯

Happy Birthday to you!

birthday

J ◯

cylinder

10 ◯

ladder

9 ◯

ladybug

8 ◯

middle

7 ◯

radio

6 ◯

radish

5 ◯

sundae

4 ◯

tadpole

3 ◯

under

2 ◯

window

medial /d/
50 Quick-Play Articulation Games

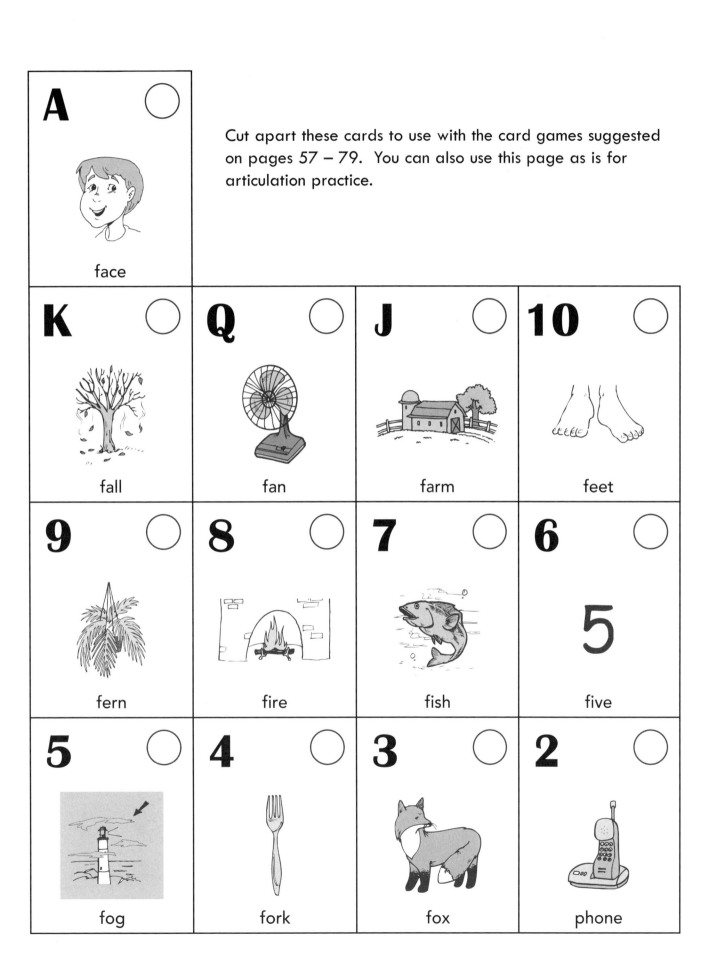

A ○

face

Cut apart these cards to use with the card games suggested on pages 57 – 79. You can also use this page as is for articulation practice.

K ○

fall

Q ○

fan

J ○

farm

10 ○

feet

9 ○

fern

8 ○

fire

7 ○

fish

6 ○

five

5 ○

fog

4 ○

fork

3 ○

fox

2 ○

phone

initial /f/ — 1 syllable
50 Quick-Play Articulation Games

115

Copyright © 2003 LinguiSystems, Inc.

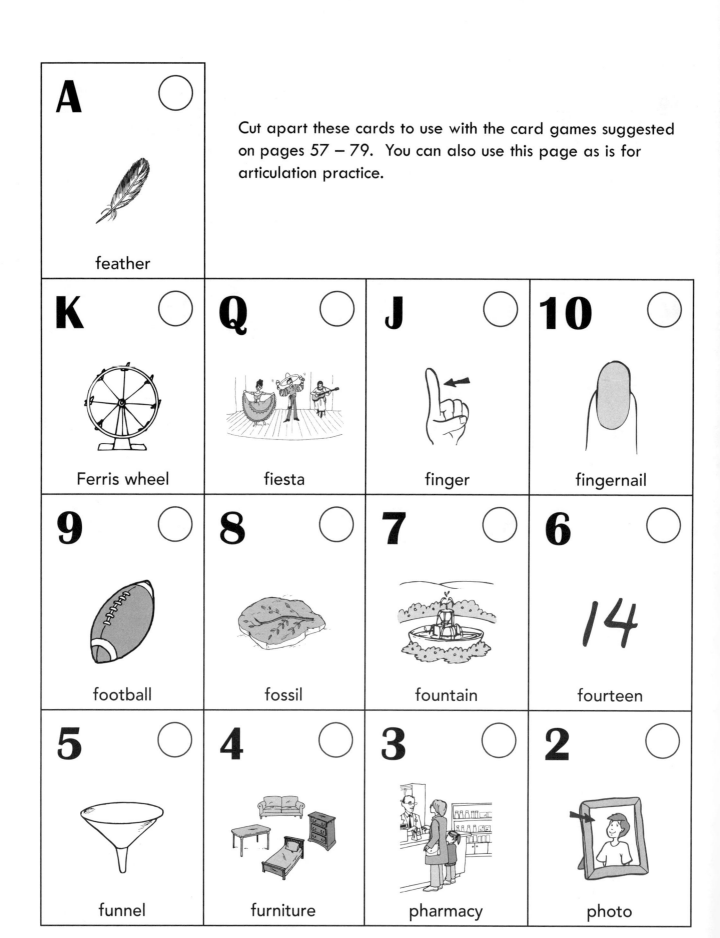

A ◯

feather

Cut apart these cards to use with the card games suggested on pages 57 – 79. You can also use this page as is for articulation practice.

K ◯

Ferris wheel

Q ◯

fiesta

J ◯

finger

10 ◯

fingernail

9 ◯

football

8 ◯

fossil

7 ◯

fountain

6 ◯

fourteen

5 ◯

funnel

4 ◯

furniture

3 ◯

pharmacy

2 ◯

photo

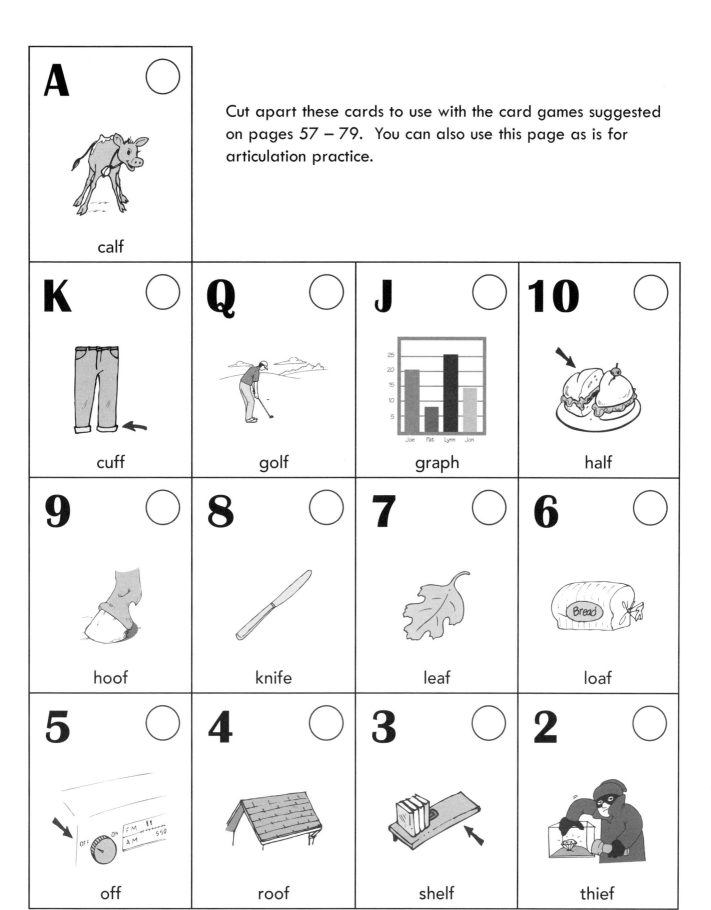

A ⬭

calf

Cut apart these cards to use with the card games suggested on pages 57 – 79. You can also use this page as is for articulation practice.

K ⬭

cuff

Q ⬭

golf

J ⬭

graph

10 ⬭

half

9 ⬭

hoof

8 ⬭

knife

7 ⬭

leaf

6 ⬭

loaf

5 ⬭

off

4 ⬭

roof

3 ⬭

shelf

2 ⬭

thief

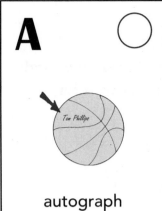

A

autograph

Cut apart these cards to use with the card games suggested on pages 57 – 79. You can also use this page as is for articulation practice.

K
bookshelf

Q
coral reef

J
dandruff

10
enough

9
giraffe

8
jackknife

7
Joseph

6
kickoff

5
paragraph

4
sheriff

3
sunroof

2
take off

A ◯

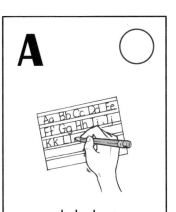

alphabet

Cut apart these cards to use with the card games suggested on pages 57 – 79. You can also use this page as is for articulation practice.

K ◯

barefoot

Q ◯

breakfast

J ◯

buffalo

10 ◯

campfire

9 ◯

daffodil

8 ◯

dolphin

7 ◯

x-ray

hyphen

6 ◯

lifeguard

5 ◯

muffin

4 ◯

office

3 ◯

pitchfork

2 ◯

refrigerator

A ◯

van

Cut apart these cards to use with the card games suggested on pages 57 – 79. You can also use this page as is for articulation practice.

K ◯

vase

Q ◯

vat

J ◯

veil

10 ◯

vein

9 ◯

vent

8 ◯

Jill fell down.

verb

7 ◯

vest

6 ◯

vet

5 ◯

vine

4 ◯

vise

3 ◯

voice

2 ◯

vote

A ⬤

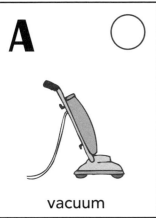

vacuum

Cut apart these cards to use with the card games suggested on pages 57 – 79. You can also use this page as is for articulation practice.

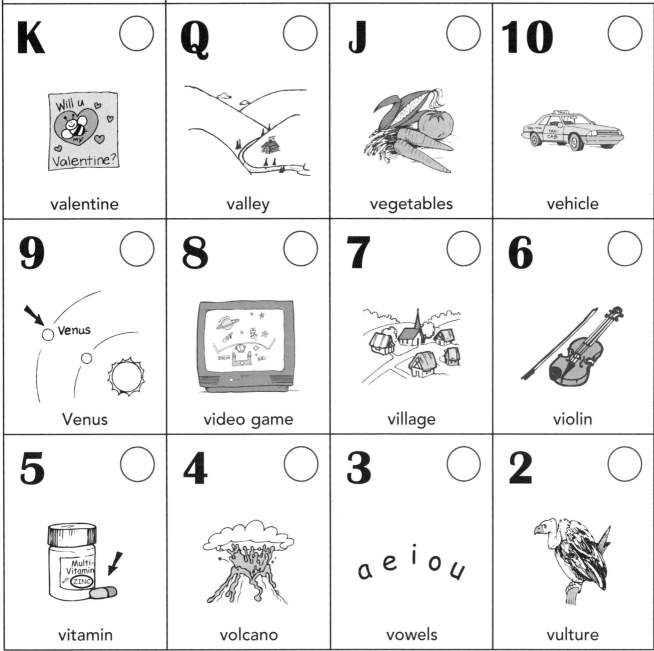

K ⬤	**Q** ⬤	**J** ⬤	**10** ⬤
valentine	valley	vegetables	vehicle
9 ⬤	**8** ⬤	**7** ⬤	**6** ⬤
Venus	video game	village	violin
5 ⬤	**4** ⬤	**3** ⬤	**2** ⬤
vitamin	volcano	vowels	vulture

A ◯

cave

Cut apart these cards to use with the card games suggested on pages 57 – 79. You can also use this page as is for articulation practice.

K ◯

drive

Q ◯

5

five

J ◯

hive

10 ◯

love

9 ◯

move

8 ◯

pave

7 ◯

shave

6 ◯

shove

5 ◯

sleeve

4 ◯

stove

3 ◯

12

twelve

2 ◯

wave

A ⭕ 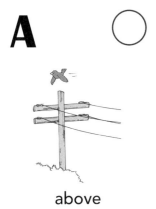 above	Cut apart these cards to use with the card games suggested on pages 57 – 79. You can also use this page as is for articulation practice.

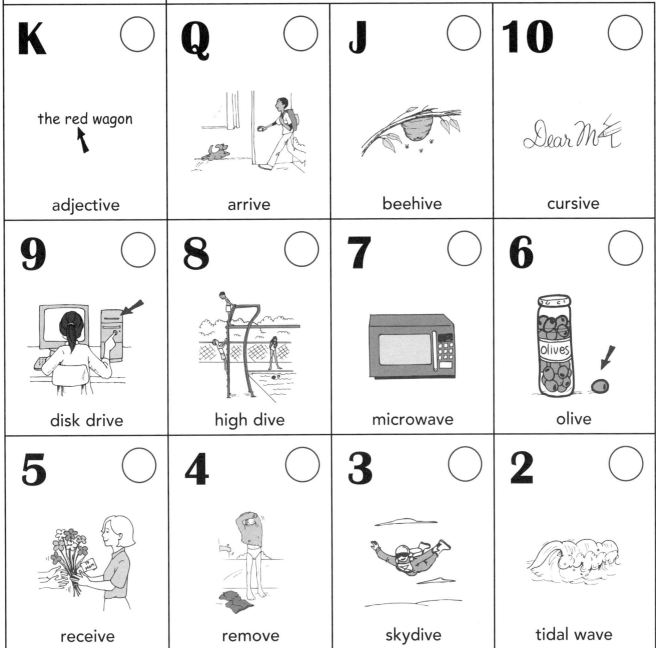

K ⭕ the red wagon ↑ adjective	**Q** ⭕ arrive	**J** ⭕ beehive	**10** ⭕ *Dear M* cursive
9 ⭕ disk drive	**8** ⭕ high dive	**7** ⭕ microwave	**6** ⭕ olives olive
5 ⭕ receive	**4** ⭕ remove	**3** ⭕ skydive	**2** ⭕ tidal wave

final /v/ — multisyllable
50 Quick-Play Articulation Games

123

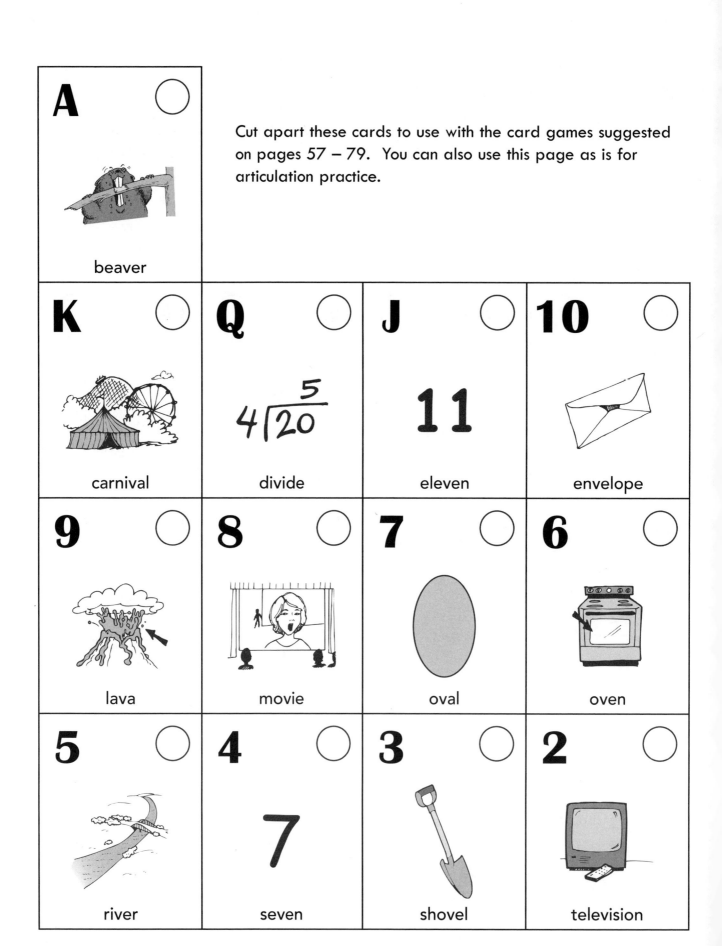

A ⃝

beaver

Cut apart these cards to use with the card games suggested on pages 57 – 79. You can also use this page as is for articulation practice.

K ⃝

carnival

Q ⃝

$4\overline{)20}$ 5

divide

J ⃝

11

eleven

10 ⃝

envelope

9 ⃝

lava

8 ⃝

movie

7 ⃝

oval

6 ⃝

oven

5 ⃝

river

4 ⃝

7

seven

3 ⃝

shovel

2 ⃝

television

A ⬭

thick

Cut apart these cards to use with the card games suggested on pages 57 – 79. You can also use this page as is for articulation practice.

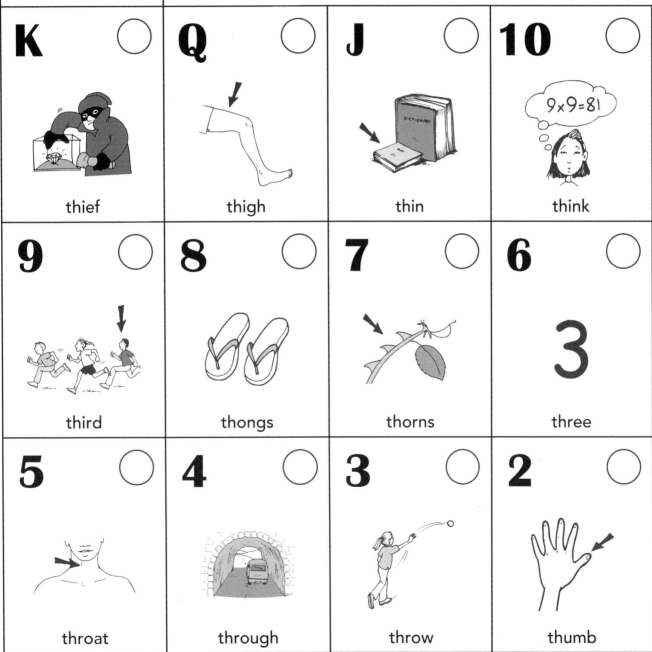

K ⬭	**Q** ⬭	**J** ⬭	**10** ⬭
thief	thigh	thin	think

9 ⬭	**8** ⬭	**7** ⬭	**6** ⬭
third	thongs	thorns	three

5 ⬭	**4** ⬭	**3** ⬭	**2** ⬭
throat	through	throw	thumb

A ◯

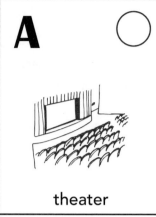

theater

Cut apart these cards to use with the card games suggested on pages 57 – 79. You can also use this page as is for articulation practice.

K ◯	Q ◯	J ◯	10 ◯
thermometer	thermos	thermostat	thimble

9 ◯	8 ◯	7 ◯	6 ◯
13	30		
thirteen	thirty	thistles	thorax

5 ◯	4 ◯	3 ◯	2 ◯
thorny	thumbtack	thunderstorm	Thursday

A ○

bath

Cut apart these cards to use with the card games suggested on pages 57 – 79. You can also use this page as is for articulation practice.

K ○	**Q** ○	**J** ○	**10** ○
booth	cloth	Earth	fourth
9 ○ math	**8** ○ month	**7** ○ mouth	**6** ○ north
5 ○ path	**4** ○ teeth	**3** ○ tooth	**2** ○ wreath

final /th/ voiceless — 1 syllable
50 Quick-Play Articulation Games

A ◯

baby tooth

Cut apart these cards to use with the card games suggested on pages 57 – 79. You can also use this page as is for articulation practice.

K ◯

birdbath

Q ◯

bubble bath

J ◯

dishcloth

10 ◯

eyetooth

9 ◯

100th

hundredth

8 ◯

mammoth

7 ◯

7th

seventh

6 ◯

tablecloth

5 ◯

50¢

tollbooth

4 ◯

20th

twentieth

3 ◯

25th

twenty-fifth

2 ◯

underneath

A ◯

$2 + 4 = 6$

arithmetic

Cut apart these cards to use with the card games suggested on pages 57 – 79. You can also use this page as is for articulation practice.

K ◯

athlete

Q ◯

author

J ◯

bath towel

10 ◯

bathtub

9 ◯

birthday

8 ◯

math class

7 ◯

one-thirty

6 ◯

python

5 ◯

southwest

4 ◯

stethoscope

3 ◯

toothbrush

2 ◯

toothpaste

medial /th/ voiceless
50 Quick-Play Articulation Games

A ◯

that (cat)

Cut apart these cards to use with the card games suggested on pages 57 – 79. You can also use this page as is for articulation practice.

K ◯	**Q** ◯	**J** ◯	**10** ◯
the (car)	them	there	these (shoes)
9 ◯	**8** ◯	**7** ◯	**6** ◯
this (dog)	those (socks)	bathe	breathe
5 ◯	**4** ◯	**3** ◯	**2** ◯
clothe	seethe	soothe	teethe

initial and final /th/ voiced — 1 syllable
50 Quick-Play Articulation Games

130

A ◯

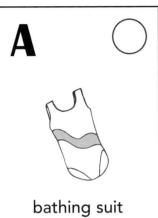

bathing suit

Cut apart these cards to use with the card games suggested on pages 57 – 79. You can also use this page as is for articulation practice.

K ◯

brother

Q ◯

clothing

J ◯

father

10 ◯

feather

9 ◯

gather

8 ◯

20>5

greater than

7 ◯

lather

6 ◯

leather

5 ◯

mother

4 ◯

tetherball

3 ◯

together

2 ◯

weather map

A ○	

shade

Cut apart these cards to use with the card games suggested on pages 57 – 79. You can also use this page as is for articulation practice.

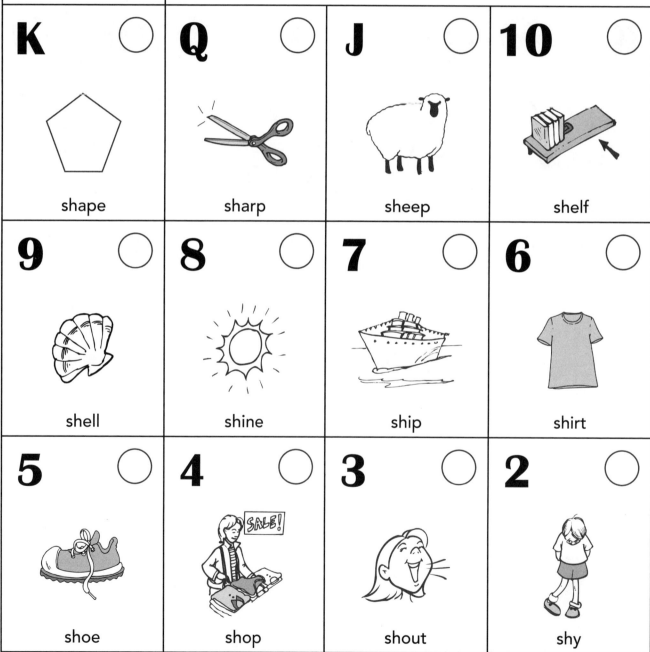

K ○	**Q** ○	**J** ○	**10** ○
shape	sharp	sheep	shelf
9 ○	**8** ○	**7** ○	**6** ○
shell	shine	ship	shirt
5 ○	**4** ○	**3** ○	**2** ○
shoe	shop	shout	shy

initial /sh/ — 1 syllable
50 Quick-Play Articulation Games

132

A ◯

shadow

Cut apart these cards to use with the card games suggested on pages 57 – 79. You can also use this page as is for articulation practice.

K ◯	**Q** ◯	**J** ◯	**10** ◯
shampoo	sharpen	shaving	shining
9 ◯	**8** ◯	**7** ◯	**6** ◯
shivering	shoelace	shopping cart	shoulder
5 ◯	**4** ◯	**3** ◯	**2** ◯
shovel	shower	shuttle	sugar

A ⃝

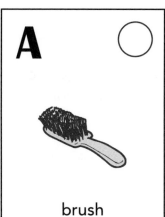

brush

Cut apart these cards to use with the card games suggested on pages 57 – 79. You can also use this page as is for articulation practice.

K ⃝	**Q** ⃝	**J** ⃝	**10** ⃝
bush	cash	crash	dish
9 ⃝	**8** ⃝	**7** ⃝	**6** ⃝
fish	flush	leash	mash
5 ⃝	**4** ⃝	**3** ⃝	**2** ⃝
smash	splash	trash	wash

A ◯

car wash

Cut apart these cards to use with the card games suggested on pages 57 – 79. You can also use this page as is for articulation practice.

K ◯	**Q** ◯	**J** ◯	**10** ◯
eyelash	finish	goldfish	hairbrush
9 ◯	**8** ◯	**7** ◯	**6** ◯
jellyfish	mustache	paintbrush	polish
5 ◯	**4** ◯	**3** ◯	**2** ◯
punish	radish	starfish	toothbrush

A ◯

addition

Cut apart these cards to use with the card games suggested on pages 57 – 79. You can also use this page as is for articulation practice.

K ◯	**Q** ◯	**J** ◯	**10** ◯
bushes	cashier	fisherman	flashlight
9 ◯	**8** ◯	**7** ◯	**6** ◯
$\frac{1}{2}$ fraction	lotion	machine	marshmallows
5 ◯	**4** ◯	**3** ◯	**2** ◯
parachute	picture	tissue	washer

A ○

chain

Cut apart these cards to use with the card games suggested on pages 57 – 79. You can also use this page as is for articulation practice.

K ○

chair

Q ○

chart

J ○

Test Today

cheat

10 ○

check

9 ○

cheek

8 ○

cheese

7 ○

chest

6 ○

chick

5 ○

child

4 ○

chin

3 ○

Potato Chips

chips

2 ○

choose

initial /ch/ — 1 syllable
50 Quick-Play Articulation Games

137

A ◯

cello

Cut apart these cards to use with the card games suggested on pages 57 – 79. You can also use this page as is for articulation practice.

K ◯	**Q** ◯	**J** ◯	**10** ◯
chalkboard	checkers	checkmark	checkup

9 ◯	**8** ◯	**7** ◯	**6** ◯
cheerful	cheetah	children	chimney

5 ◯	**4** ◯	**3** ◯	**2** ◯
chimpanzee	chipmunk	chocolate cake	chopsticks

initial /ch/ — multisyllable
50 Quick-Play Articulation Games

138

A ◯

beach

Cut apart these cards to use with the card games suggested on pages 57 – 79. You can also use this page as is for articulation practice.

K ◯ bench	**Q** ◯ bunch
J ◯ catch	**10** ◯ coach
9 ◯ inch	**8** ◯ lunch
7 ◯ patch	**6** ◯ peach
5 ◯ stretch	**4** ◯ switch
3 ◯ watch	**2** ◯ wrench

final /ch/ — 1 syllable
50 Quick-Play Articulation Games

139

A ◯

attach

Cut apart these cards to use with the card games suggested on pages 57 – 79. You can also use this page as is for articulation practice.

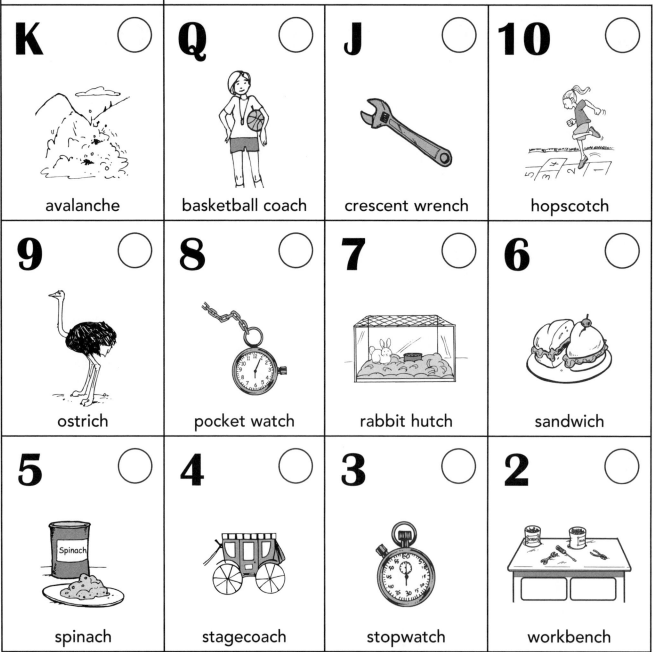

K ◯	**Q** ◯	**J** ◯	**10** ◯
avalanche	basketball coach	crescent wrench	hopscotch
9 ◯	**8** ◯	**7** ◯	**6** ◯
ostrich	pocket watch	rabbit hutch	sandwich
5 ◯	**4** ◯	**3** ◯	**2** ◯
spinach	stagecoach	stopwatch	workbench

A ◯

benches

Cut apart these cards to use with the card games suggested on pages 57 – 79. You can also use this page as is for articulation practice.

K ◯	**Q** ◯	**J** ◯	**10** ◯
catcher	crutches	furniture	inches
9 ◯	**8** ◯	**7** ◯	**6** ◯
ketchup	kitchen	pitcher	potato chips
5 ◯	**4** ◯	**3** ◯	**2** ◯
statue	teacher	vulture	wheelchair

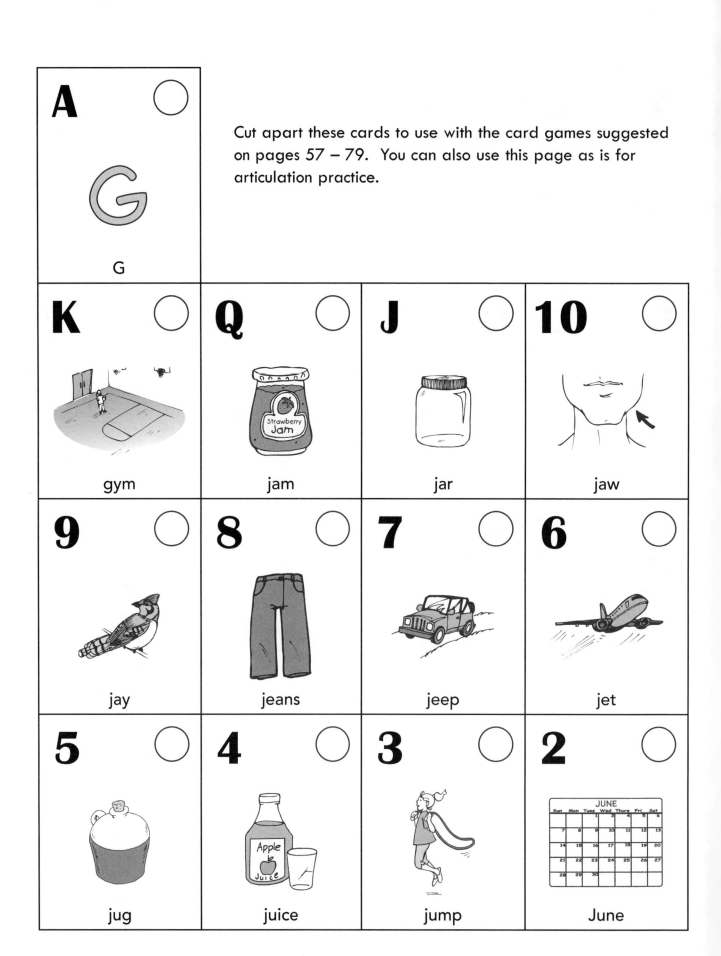

Cut apart these cards to use with the card games suggested on pages 57 – 79. You can also use this page as is for articulation practice.

A

G

G

K

gym

Q

jam

J

jar

10

jaw

9

jay

8

jeans

7

jeep

6

jet

5

jug

4

juice

3

jump

2

June

A ◯

gerbil

Cut apart these cards to use with the card games suggested on pages 57 – 79. You can also use this page as is for articulation practice.

K ◯	**Q** ◯	**J** ◯	**10** ◯
giant	giraffe	gymnasium	jacket
9 ◯	**8** ◯	**7** ◯	**6** ◯
jaguar	jelly	jellyfish	jersey
5 ◯	**4** ◯	**3** ◯	**2** ◯
jewels	jigsaw puzzle	juggle	jungle

strawberry jelly

10

initial /j/ — multisyllable
50 Quick-Play Articulation Games

A ⃝

badge

Cut apart these cards to use with the card games suggested on pages 57 – 79. You can also use this page as is for articulation practice.

K ⃝	**Q** ⃝	**J** ⃝	**10** ⃝
bridge	cage	edge	fringe
9 ⃝	**8** ⃝	**7** ⃝	**6** ⃝
fudge	hedge	large	luggage
5 ⃝	**4** ⃝	**3** ⃝	**2** ⃝
message	orange	package	page

final
50 Quic...

Games

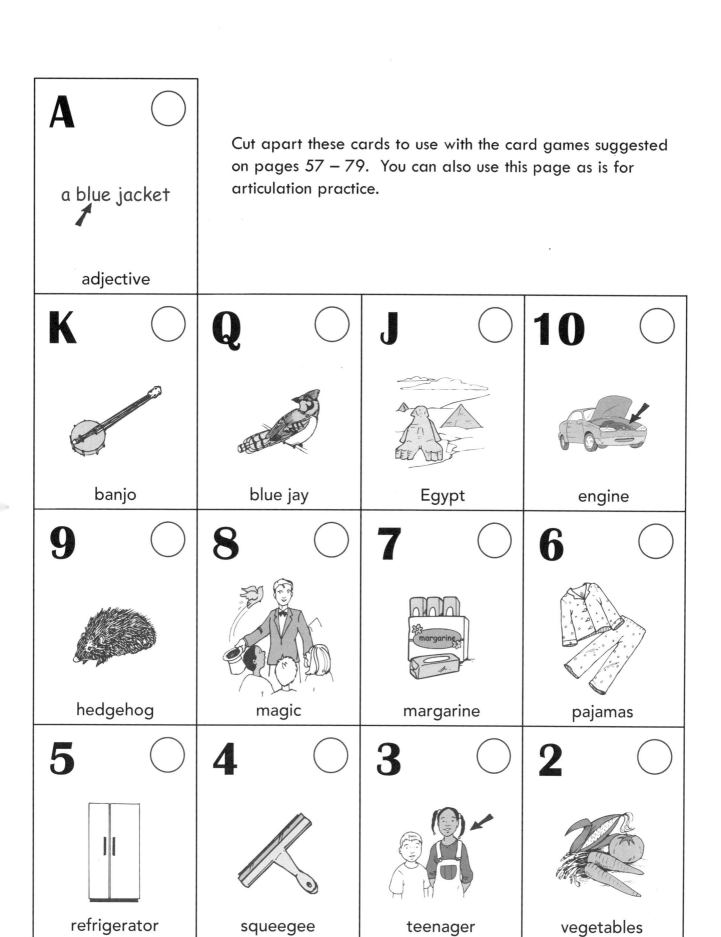

A ◯

a blue jacket ↑

adjective

Cut apart these cards to use with the card games suggested on pages 57 – 79. You can also use this page as is for articulation practice.

K ◯

banjo

Q ◯

blue jay

J ◯

Egypt

10 ◯

engine

9 ◯

hedgehog

8 ◯

magic

7 ◯

margarine

6 ◯

pajamas

5 ◯

refrigerator

4 ◯

squeegee

3 ◯

teenager

2 ◯

vegetables

A ◯

sad

Cut apart these cards to use with the card games suggested on pages 57 – 79. You can also use this page as is for articulation practice.

K ◯

same

Q ◯

saw

J ◯

sew

10 ◯

sink

9 ◯

soap

8 ◯

suit

7 ◯

sun

6 ◯

Z

5 ◯

Zach

4 ◯

zone

3 ◯

zoo

2 ◯

zoom

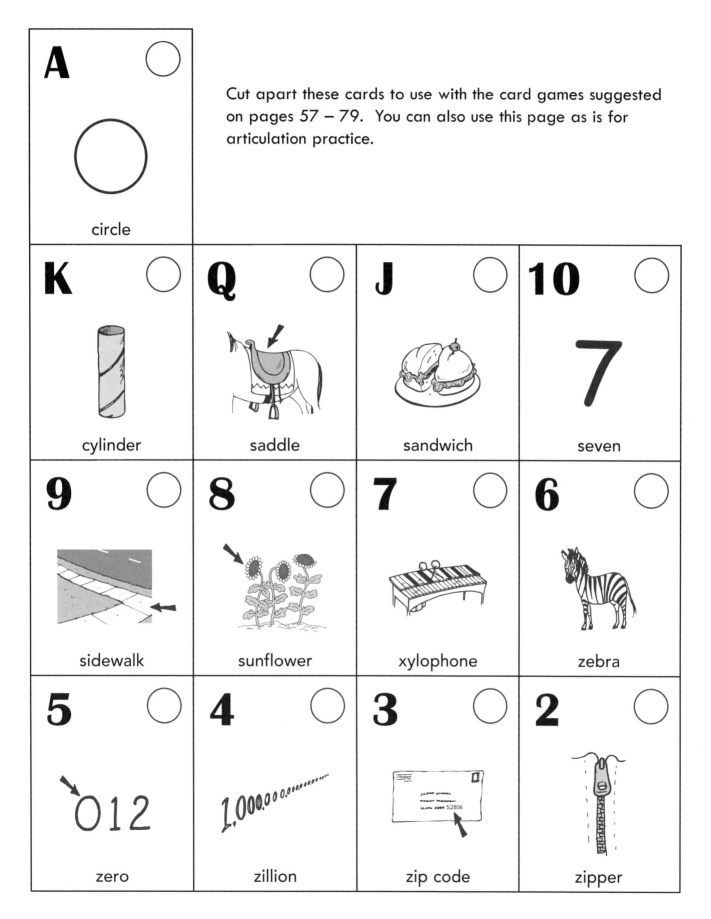

A ◯

◯

circle

Cut apart these cards to use with the card games suggested on pages 57 – 79. You can also use this page as is for articulation practice.

K ◯

cylinder

Q ◯

saddle

J ◯

sandwich

10 ◯

7

seven

9 ◯

sidewalk

8 ◯

sunflower

7 ◯

xylophone

6 ◯

zebra

5 ◯

012

zero

4 ◯

1,000,000.00000000000000

zillion

3 ◯

52806

zip code

2 ◯

zipper

A ○

boys

Cut apart these cards to use with the card games suggested on pages 57 – 79. You can also use this page as is for articulation practice.

K ○

bus

Q ○

cheese

J ○

class

10 ○

dress

9 ○

face

8 ○

fries

7 ○

goose

6 ○

house

5 ○

kiss

4 ○

nose

3 ○

sneeze

2 ○

toys

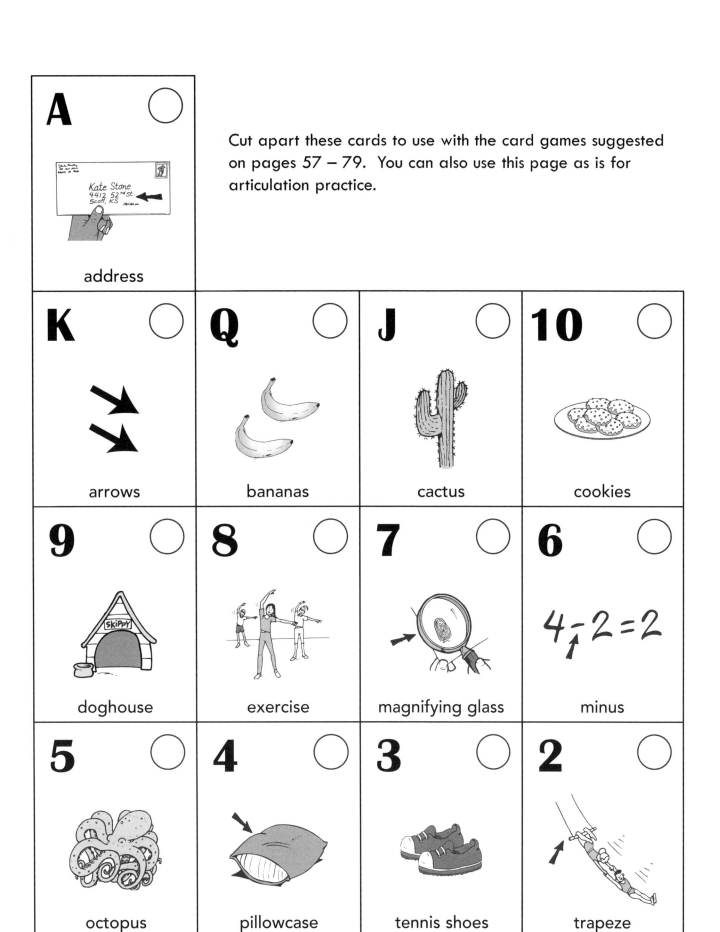

A ◯

address

Cut apart these cards to use with the card games suggested on pages 57 – 79. You can also use this page as is for articulation practice.

K ◯

arrows

Q ◯

bananas

J ◯

cactus

10 ◯

cookies

9 ◯

doghouse

8 ◯

exercise

7 ◯

magnifying glass

6 ◯

minus

5 ◯

octopus

4 ◯

pillowcase

3 ◯

tennis shoes

2 ◯

trapeze

A ◯

bicycle

Cut apart these cards to use with the card games suggested on pages 57 – 79. You can also use this page as is for articulation practice.

K ◯

closet

Q ◯

consonant

J ◯

desert

10 ◯

dinosaur

9 ◯

horizon

8 ◯

insect

7 ◯

lizard

6 ◯

messy

5 ◯

possum

4 ◯

puzzle

3 ◯

trapezoid

2 ◯

whistle

A ◯

school

Cut apart these cards to use with the card games suggested on pages 57 – 79. You can also use this page as is for articulation practice.

K ◯	**Q** ◯	**J** ◯	**10** ◯
sky	sled	slide	smile
9 ◯	**8** ◯	**7** ◯	**6** ◯
smoke	snail	snow	spoon
5 ◯	**4** ◯	**3** ◯	**2** ◯
square	stage	stalk	swan

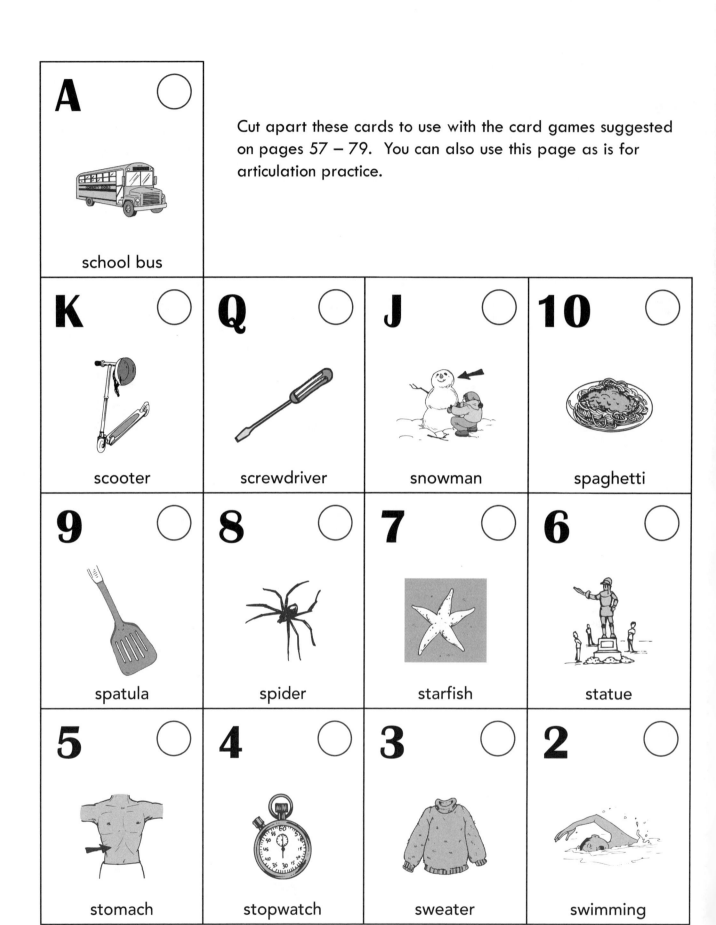

A ⃝

school bus

Cut apart these cards to use with the card games suggested on pages 57 – 79. You can also use this page as is for articulation practice.

K ⃝

scooter

Q ⃝

screwdriver

J ⃝

snowman

10 ⃝

spaghetti

9 ⃝

spatula

8 ⃝

spider

7 ⃝

starfish

6 ⃝

statue

5 ⃝

stomach

4 ⃝

stopwatch

3 ⃝

sweater

2 ⃝

swimming

A ◯

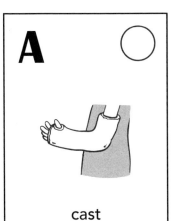

cast

Cut apart these cards to use with the card games suggested on pages 57 – 79. You can also use this page as is for articulation practice.

K ◯	**Q** ◯	**J** ◯	**10** ◯
clasp	desk	disk	east
9 ◯	**8** ◯	**7** ◯	**6** ◯
first	list	nest	tusk
5 ◯	**4** ◯	**3** ◯	**2** ◯
vest	wasp	whisk	wrist

final /s/ blends — 1 syllable
50 Quick-Play Articulation Games

153

A ○

artist

Cut apart these cards to use with the card games suggested on pages 57 – 79. You can also use this page as is for articulation practice.

K ○	**Q** ○	**J** ○	**10** ○
breakfast	dentist	forest	gymnast
9 ○	**8** ○	**7** ○	**6** ○
littlest	northeast	northwest	scientist
5 ○	**4** ○	**3** ○	**2** ○
southeast	southwest	toothpaste	ventriloquist

A ◯

Jill's essay
won the prize.

apostrophe

Cut apart these cards to use with the card games suggested on pages 57 – 79. You can also use this page as is for articulation practice.

K ◯	**Q** ◯	**J** ◯	**10** ◯
asleep	astronaut	basket	bracelet
9 ◯	**8** ◯	**7** ◯	**6** ◯
costume	escalator	hopscotch	instruments
5 ◯	**4** ◯	**3** ◯	**2** ◯
microscope	United States	whisper	yardstick

medial /s/ blends
50 Quick-Play Articulation Games

A ◯

lamb

Cut apart these cards to use with the card games suggested on pages 57 – 79. You can also use this page as is for articulation practice.

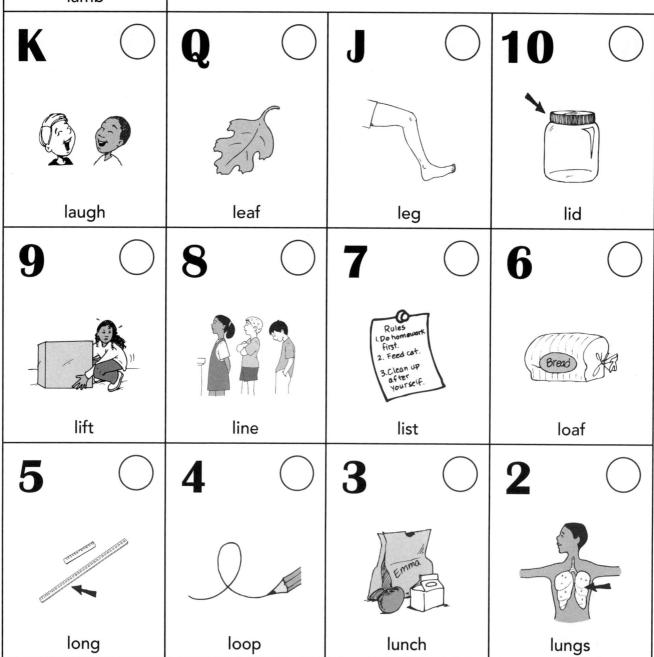

K ◯

laugh

Q ◯

leaf

J ◯

leg

10 ◯

lid

9 ◯

lift

8 ◯

line

7 ◯

list

6 ◯

loaf

5 ◯

long

4 ◯

loop

3 ◯

lunch

2 ◯

lungs

A ◯

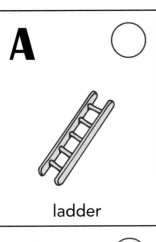

ladder

Cut apart these cards to use with the card games suggested on pages 57 – 79. You can also use this page as is for articulation practice.

K ◯	**Q** ◯	**J** ◯	**10** ◯
lawnmower	lemon	leopard	letter
9 ◯	**8** ◯	**7** ◯	**6** ◯
library	lifeguard	lightning	limousine
5 ◯	**4** ◯	**3** ◯	**2** ◯
litterbug	lizard	lockers	lumber

initial /l/ — multisyllable
50 Quick-Play Articulation Games

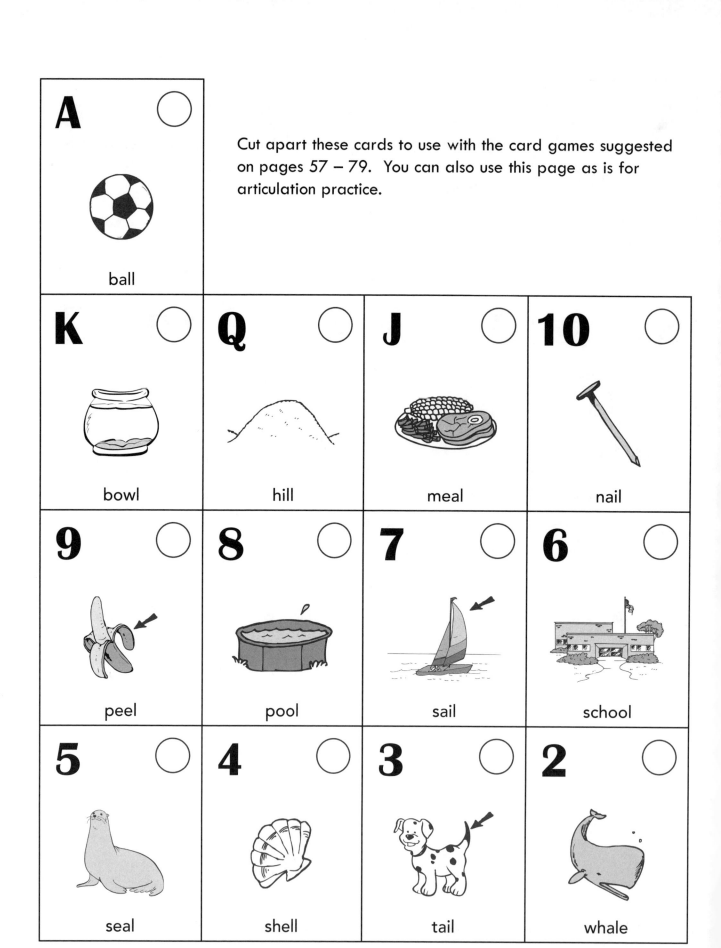

A — ball

Cut apart these cards to use with the card games suggested on pages 57 – 79. You can also use this page as is for articulation practice.

K — bowl

Q — hill

J — meal

10 — nail

9 — peel

8 — pool

7 — sail

6 — school

5 — seal

4 — shell

3 — tail

2 — whale

A ◯	Cut apart these cards to use with the card games suggested on pages 57 – 79. You can also use this page as is for articulation practice.

apple

K ◯	**Q** ◯	**J** ◯	**10** ◯
basketball	cereal	circle	easel

9 ◯	**8** ◯	**7** ◯	**6** ◯
fossil	jungle	middle	pencil

5 ◯	**4** ◯	**3** ◯	**2** ◯
table	tadpole	vowel	windmill

final /l/ — multisyllable
50 Quick-Play Articulation Games

A ◯

alarm

Cut apart these cards to use with the card games suggested on pages 57 – 79. You can also use this page as is for articulation practice.

K ◯ balloon	**Q** ◯ bowling	**J** ◯ calendar	**10** ◯ cylinder
9 ◯ elevator	**8** ◯ island	**7** ◯ pillow	**6** ◯ shoelace
5 ◯ telescope	**4** ◯ umbrella	**3** ◯ violin	**2** ◯ wallet

A ◯

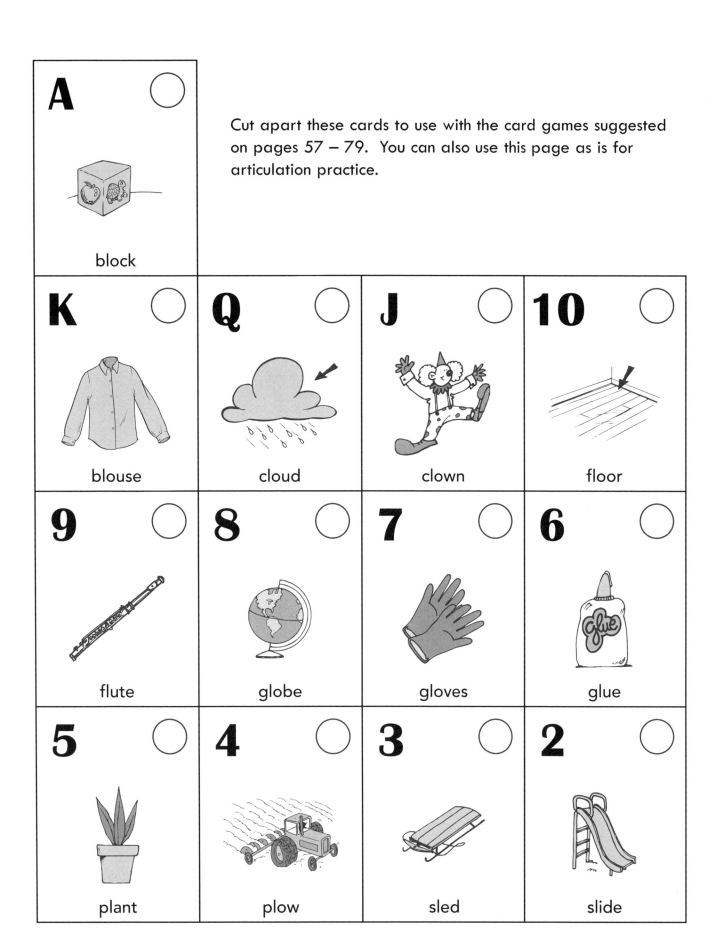

block

Cut apart these cards to use with the card games suggested on pages 57 – 79. You can also use this page as is for articulation practice.

K ◯
blouse

Q ◯
cloud

J ◯
clown

10 ◯
floor

9 ◯
flute

8 ◯
globe

7 ◯
gloves

6 ◯
glue

5 ◯
plant

4 ◯
plow

3 ◯
sled

2 ◯
slide

initial /l/ blends — 1 syllable
50 Quick-Play Articulation Games

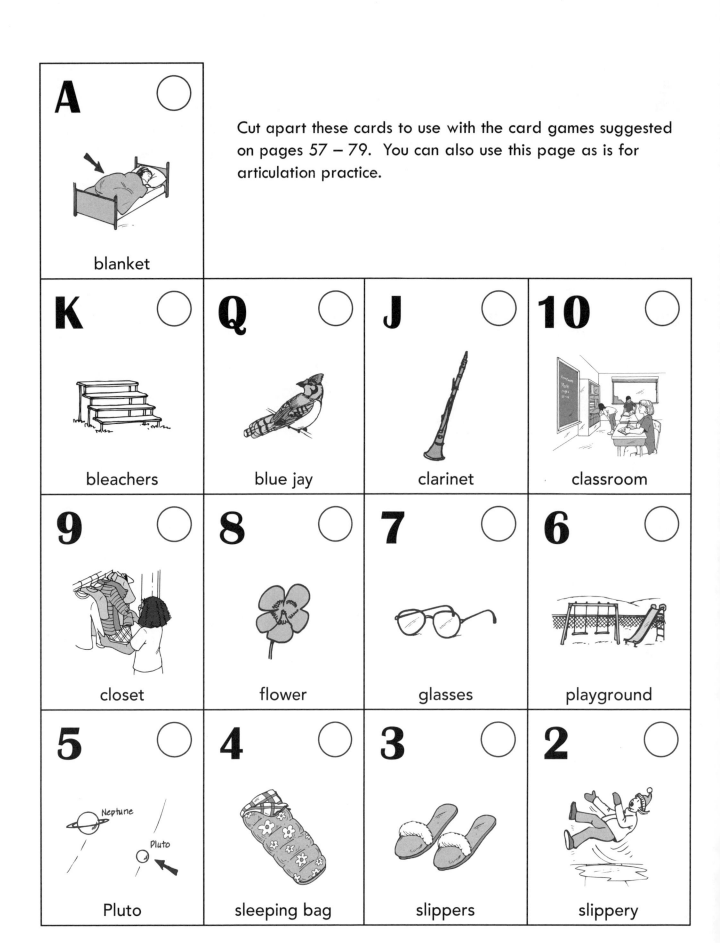

Cut apart these cards to use with the card games suggested on pages 57 – 79. You can also use this page as is for articulation practice.

A blanket			
K bleachers	**Q** blue jay	**J** clarinet	**10** classroom
9 closet	**8** flower	**7** glasses	**6** playground
5 Pluto	**4** sleeping bag	**3** slippers	**2** slippery

A ◯

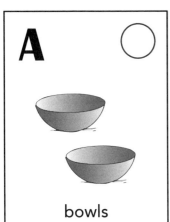

bowls

Cut apart these cards to use with the card games suggested on pages 57 – 79. You can also use this page as is for articulation practice.

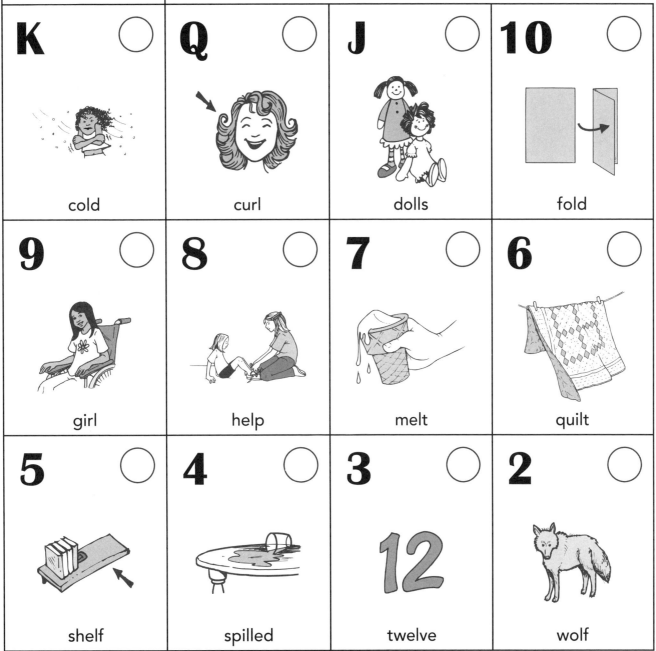

K ◯	**Q** ◯	**J** ◯	**10** ◯
cold	curl	dolls	fold
9 ◯	**8** ◯	**7** ◯	**6** ◯
girl	help	melt	quilt
5 ◯	**4** ◯	**3** ◯	**2** ◯
shelf	spilled	twelve	wolf

final /l/ blends — 1 syllable
50 Quick-Play Articulation Games

A ◯

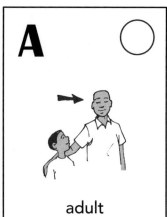

adult

Cut apart these cards to use with the card games suggested on pages 57 – 79. You can also use this page as is for articulation practice.

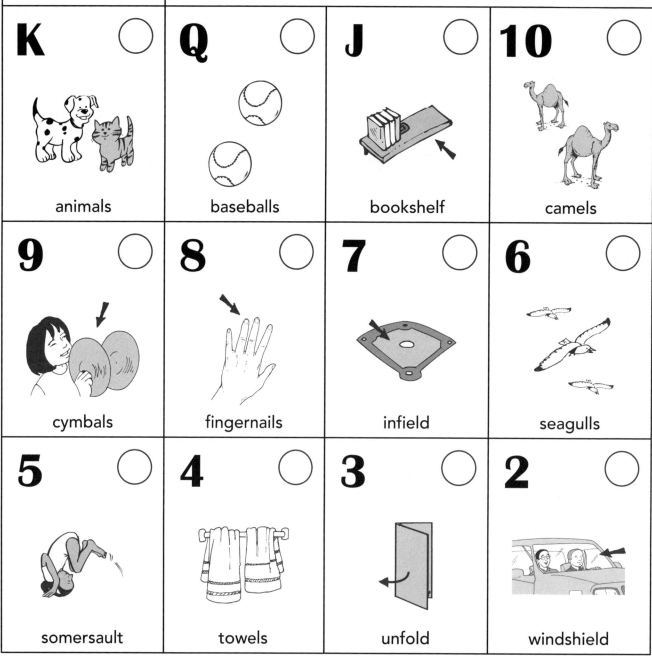

K ◯	**Q** ◯	**J** ◯	**10** ◯
animals	baseballs	bookshelf	camels

9 ◯	**8** ◯	**7** ◯	**6** ◯
cymbals	fingernails	infield	seagulls

5 ◯	**4** ◯	**3** ◯	**2** ◯
somersault	towels	unfold	windshield

final /l/ blends — multisyllable
50 Quick-Play Articulation Games

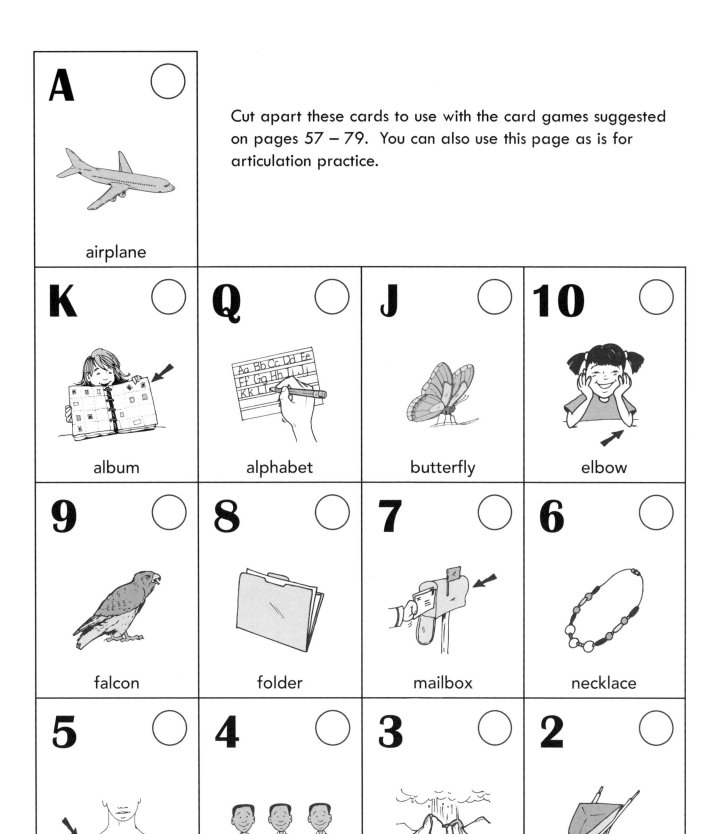

A ◯

airplane

Cut apart these cards to use with the card games suggested on pages 57 – 79. You can also use this page as is for articulation practice.

K ◯

album

Q ◯

alphabet

J ◯

butterfly

10 ◯

elbow

9 ◯

falcon

8 ◯

folder

7 ◯

mailbox

6 ◯

necklace

5 ◯

shoulder

4 ◯

triplets

3 ◯

volcano

2 ◯

wheelbarrow

A ○

race

Cut apart these cards to use with the card games suggested on pages 57 – 79. You can also use this page as is for articulation practice.

K ○	**Q** ○	**J** ○	**10** ○
rain	rake	rat	read
9 ○	**8** ○	**7** ○	**6** ○
rib	ring	road	roof
5 ○	**4** ○	**3** ○	**2** ○
root	rope	rose	rug

A ○

raccoon

Cut apart these cards to use with the card games suggested on pages 57 – 79. You can also use this page as is for articulation practice.

K ○	**Q** ○	**J** ○	**10** ○
radio	radish	rainbow	rattle
9 ○	**8** ○	**7** ○	**6** ○
rattlesnake	ravine	rectangle	reptile
5 ○	**4** ○	**3** ○	**2** ○
ribbon	robot	Rocky Mountains	writing

initial /r/ — multisyllable
50 Quick-Play Articulation Games

167

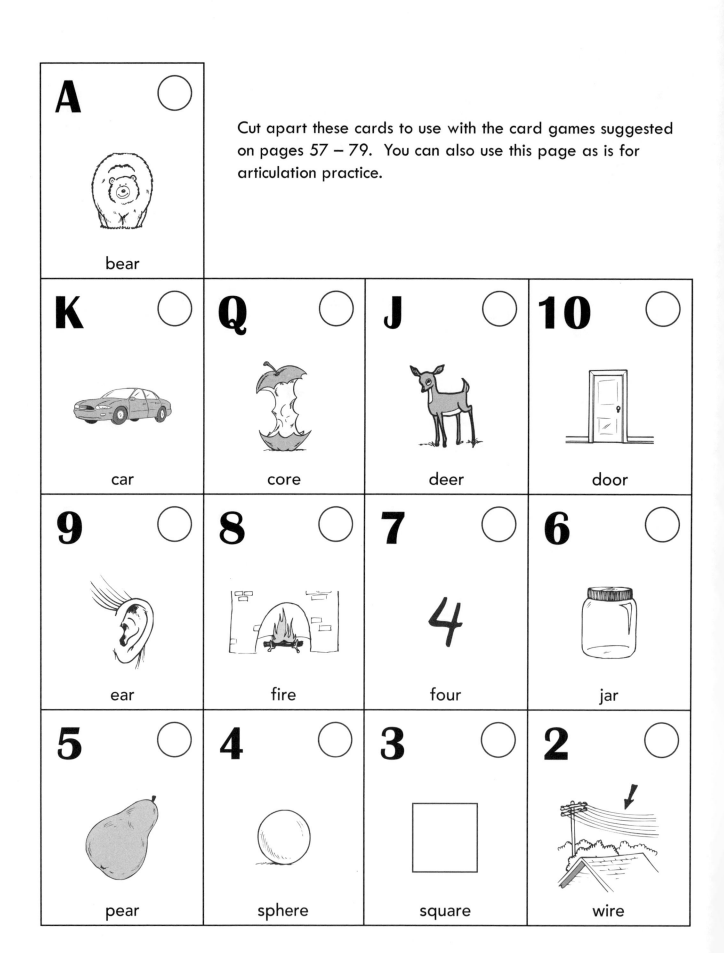

A ◯

bear

Cut apart these cards to use with the card games suggested on pages 57 – 79. You can also use this page as is for articulation practice.

K ◯

car

Q ◯

core

J ◯

deer

10 ◯

door

9 ◯

ear

8 ◯

fire

7 ◯

four

6 ◯

jar

5 ◯

pear

4 ◯

sphere

3 ◯

square

2 ◯

wire

A ⃝

bookstore

Cut apart these cards to use with the card games suggested on pages 57 – 79. You can also use this page as is for articulation practice.

K ⃝	**Q** ⃝	**J** ⃝	**10** ⃝
boxcar	campfire	cashier	diameter
9 ⃝	**8** ⃝	**7** ⃝	**6** ⃝
dinosaur	equator	guitar	handlebar
5 ⃝	**4** ⃝	**3** ⃝	**2** ⃝
mother	pioneer	water	wheelchair

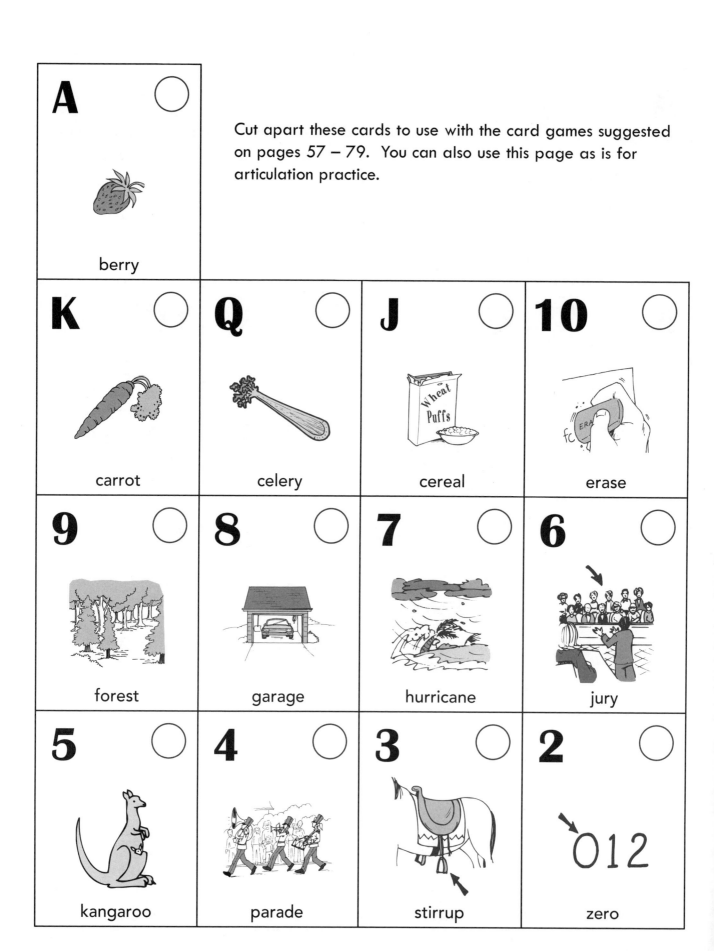

A ⃝

berry

Cut apart these cards to use with the card games suggested on pages 57 – 79. You can also use this page as is for articulation practice.

K ⃝

carrot

Q ⃝

celery

J ⃝

cereal

10 ⃝

erase

9 ⃝

forest

8 ⃝

garage

7 ⃝

hurricane

6 ⃝

jury

5 ⃝

kangaroo

4 ⃝

parade

3 ⃝

stirrup

2 ⃝

zero

A ◯

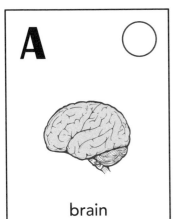

brain

Cut apart these cards to use with the card games suggested on pages 57 – 79. You can also use this page as is for articulation practice.

K ◯	**Q** ◯	**J** ◯	**10** ◯
bridge	crane	crow	drink
9 ◯	**8** ◯	**7** ◯	**6** ◯
drum	frog	grape	grill
5 ◯	**4** ◯	**3** ◯	**2** ◯
price	print	tree	truck

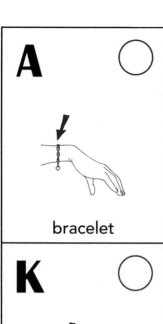

A ◯

bracelet

Cut apart these cards to use with the card games suggested on pages 57 – 79. You can also use this page as is for articulation practice.

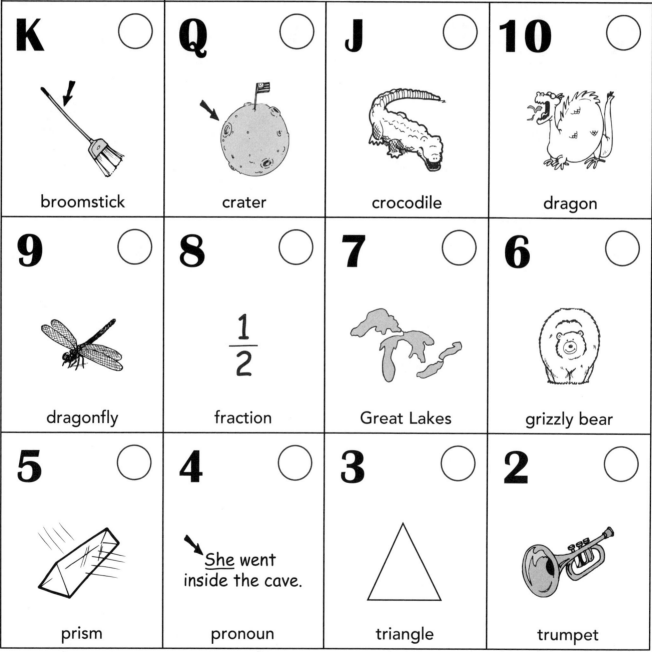

K ◯

broomstick

Q ◯

crater

J ◯

crocodile

10 ◯

dragon

9 ◯

dragonfly

8 ◯

$\frac{1}{2}$

fraction

7 ◯

Great Lakes

6 ◯

grizzly bear

5 ◯

prism

4 ◯

She went inside the cave.

pronoun

3 ◯

triangle

2 ◯

trumpet

initial /r/ blends — multisyllable
50 Quick-Play Articulation Games

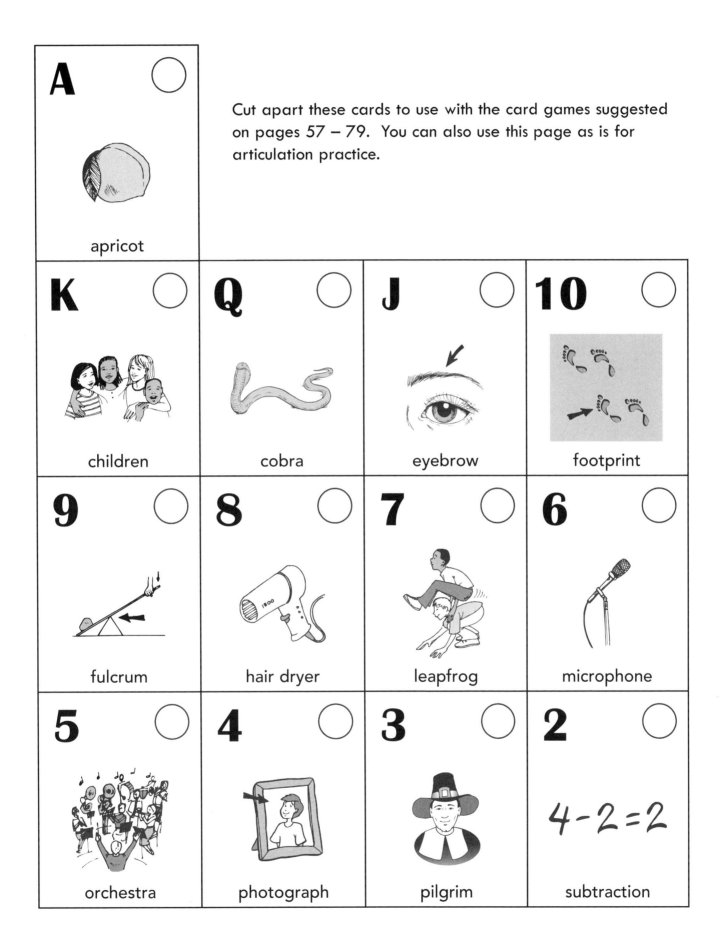

A ◯

apricot

Cut apart these cards to use with the card games suggested on pages 57 – 79. You can also use this page as is for articulation practice.

K ◯

children

Q ◯

cobra

J ◯

eyebrow

10 ◯

footprint

9 ◯

fulcrum

8 ◯

hair dryer

7 ◯

leapfrog

6 ◯

microphone

5 ◯

orchestra

4 ◯

photograph

3 ◯

pilgrim

2 ◯

4-2=2

subtraction

Non-Competitive Games

(Articulation cards are on pages 80–173. Any of these activities can be adapted so that your student can practice at the word, phrase, or sentence level.)

Beanbag Game

Scatter 10–20 articulation cards faceup on the floor. Have students take turns tossing a beanbag onto the cards and saying the word on the card that it lands on. Play continues until all cards have been landed on at least once.

Category Game

Give each student the same number of articulation cards. Choose a student to go first. This student takes a card from his hand, places it on the table faceup, and names it along with its category. For example, "____ is a _____." The first person to say another item in the category then takes a turn. She chooses a card from her hand, names it and its category, etc. Play continues until all the cards are gone.

Memory Game

Have students say a phrase like "I'm going on vacation and I'm taking a ___" or "I'm going on a picnic and I'm bringing ____" and fill in the blank with a word with their target sound. The next student needs to repeat what the previous student said and add another item with her target sound. This game works well with groups of students working on the same sound or a variety of speech sounds. You can use the articulation cards to help students remember all items said or encourage students to remember all items said. Play continues until students go through all of the articulation cards or until they can't remember the items said.

I Spy

Arrange 10–20 articulation cards faceup on the table in a grid pattern with rows and columns. One player gives clues like "I spy with my little eye something that is (____)." Depending on the level of practice, another student can guess by saying the word that matches the clue (_____) or put it in a sentence like "Is it a (_____)?" The student who guesses correctly takes the next turn. Play continues until all cards have been "spied."

Rhyming Game

Place a stack of articulation cards facedown on the table. Have a student turn over the top card and tell what rhymes with the target word like "_____ rhymes with _____." If the student can't think of a rhyming word, have him make up a silly nonsense word that rhymes with it or pass the card to another student of his choice. Play continues until all of the articulation cards have been practiced.

continued on next page

Same or Different

Scatter 10–20 articulation cards faceup on the table. Point to two pictures. Have one student say how the two things are different and another student tell how they are the same. Remind both students to use their target sounds correctly in their sentences. Play continues until you have practiced all the articulation cards.

Shine a Light

Put articulation cards or items containing the target sound(s) around the room or along a chalkboard ledge. Then turn off the lights. Have students take turns shining the flashlight on one of the cards/items and saying the word. Play continues until all cards have been practiced.

Silly Dice Game

Use the dice from pages 176–177. Your students will have fun practicing their articulation while they do silly actions.

Sorting Game

Put articulation cards or items (some with and some without the target sound) in a box or bag. As the student takes the cards/items out of the box, have her name each one and sort them by whether or not they have the target sound. This activity is good for discrimination work. Play continues until all cards/items are removed from the box.

Tongue Twister

Using a list of target words or pictures, challenge your students to see how many target words they can put in one sentence. Write down the sentences for later practice.

What Goes With It?

Place 5–10 articulation cards faceup on the table. Point to one of the cards and ask the student to tell what goes with the target word like "A _____ goes with a _____." Once the student has answered, have that student turn the card facedown and choose another card for the next student. Play continues until all the cards are facedown.

50 Quick-Play Articulation Games

Silly Dice

Use this die to play the Silly Dice Game described on page 175. Cut out the cube pattern below and on page 177 along the solid lines. Then fold them along the dotted lines and tape or glue the tabs together to make two cubes. Have students roll both dice to practice their articulation. They will have fun doing the silly actions while practicing their articulation. If you prefer not to have your students do the silly actions, only use the die on page 177.

For additional practice, you can customize the die by cutting out the die pattern, turning it over, writing your directions on the back, and then taping or gluing it together wrong-side out to make a cube.

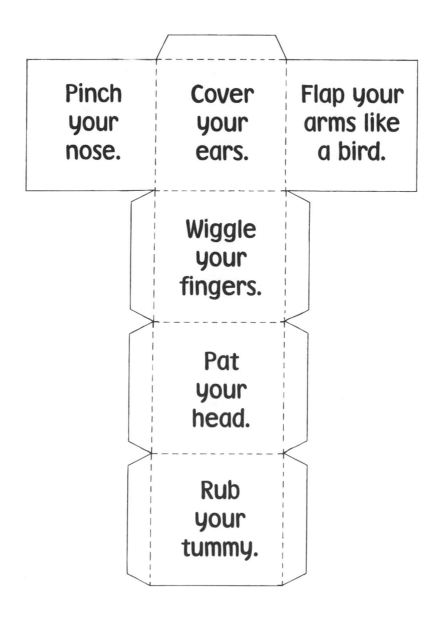

50 Quick-Play Articulation Games

Use this die to play the Silly Dice Game described on page 175. Cut out the die pattern along the solid lines. Then fold it along the dotted lines and tape or glue the tabs together to make a cube. Use this die with the die on page 176.

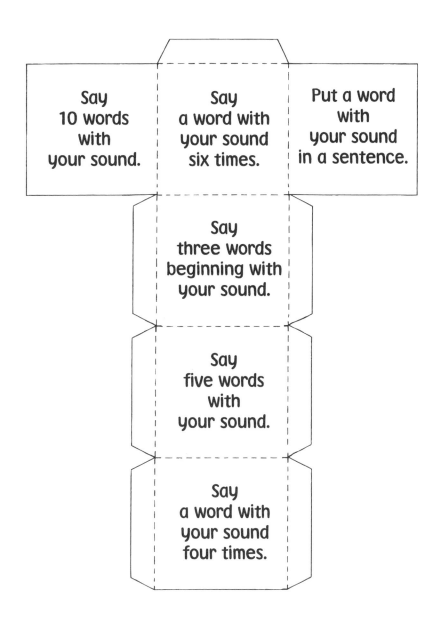

Say
10 words
with
your sound.

Say
a word with
your sound
six times.

Put a word
with
your sound
in a sentence.

Say
three words
beginning with
your sound.

Say
five words
with
your sound.

Say
a word with
your sound
four times.

50 Quick-Play Articulation Games

Help Froggie get home to his lilypad. Remember to say your sound correctly.

Catch a fly.
Lose a turn.

Slip in
the water.
Lose a turn.

Target the Stars

Color a star each time you say your word/sentence correctly ___ times.

50 Quick-Play Articulation Games

References

Costello, M. J. 1991. *The Greatest Games of All Time.* NY: John Wiley & Sons, Inc.

McLeod, J. *Classified Index of Card Games.* <http://www.pagat.com/class/index.html> (September 3, 2002).

Mohr, M. S. 1993. *The Games Treasury.* Shelburne, VT: Chapters Publishing Ltd.

Rasa, R. 2002. <*www.solitairecentral.com*> (September 9, 2002).
    This Web site provides directions for many different kinds of solitaire games.

Whiskeyman, L. & Truman, B. 2003. *No-Glamour Articulation.* East Moline, IL: LinguiSystems, Inc.

<http://www.bright.net/~mile505/Childrens/Children.html> *Children's Card Games.* (September 3, 2002).

<http://www.learningstreet.org/resources> (September 9, 2002). "Learning Street—An online resource from McRel." (2000). This Web site contains lists of subject matter terms and phrases for grade-level spans and also grade level vocabulary lists organized into semantic clusters (i.e., groups of related words).

26-07-9876

50 Quick-Play Articulation Games